PHILADELPHIA MEDICA

Being a Guide to the City's
Historical Places of Health Interest

BY

JOHN FRANCIS MARION

SMITHKLINE CORPORATION

Distributed by Stackpole Books,
Cameron and Kelker Streets, Harrisburg, PA 17105

ACKNOWLEDGMENTS

In the writing of any book, there are always those who enable the author to visualize clearly the work before him and who provide the initial impetus. In this instance, I must acknowledge my debt to the late Leo Riordan, for many years a distinguished Philadelphia journalist and later historian at Thomas Jefferson University. He was sympathetic, understanding and completely unselfish in sharing his knowledge of Philadelphia medical history with me. He suggested the paths for me to take. It is my great regret that he did not live to see the book in print.

Other friends and associates provided little-known information, unearthed books difficult to find and were constantly helpful in my quest. They include: Seymour Adelman, Barbara S. Bates, Joseph and Madeline Fox, Bernard Friedman, M.S. in Ph., Dorothy S. Kussmaul, Anne M. Morley, Joseph E. and Ruth Branning Molloy, Constance O'Hara, Jean L. Rapp, Wilmer Roberts, Florence F. Robertson, Jerome Rubin, Alice Smith and Katharine R. Boucot Sturgis, M.D.

At specific institutions they were: American Philosophical Society Library, Whitfield J. Bell, Jr., Roy E. Goodman, Carl F. Miller, Hildegard G. Stephans and Jean T. Williams; The College of Physicians of Philadelphia, Lynn DeCaro; Friends Hospital, William P. Camp, M.D., and Melissa Johnson; Hahnemann Medical Center Library, Janice Clark and Barbara Williams; the Institute of Pennsylvania Hospital, Edith Elliott and Robert E. Jones, M.D.; Nazareth Hospital, Ralph Manko; Pennsylvania College of Optometry, Richard C. Schiller, O.D.; Philadelphia College of Osteopathic Medicine, Barbara Sigman; Philadelphia City Institute, Free Library of Philadelphia, Paul McAdam; *The Philadelphia Inquirer,* Eleanor Gaynon; the School of Veterinary Medicine, University of Pennsylvania, Fannie K. Apple and Joseph F. Skelley, V.M.D.; Navy Regional Medical Center, Rear Admiral Robert L. Baker, MC, USN; Temple University Health Sciences Center, Frank J. Avato; Temple University, Samuel Paley Library, Miriam I. Crawford and Thomas M. Whitehead; and Thomas Jefferson University, Oliver W. Robbins.

I am especially grateful to all those who have read the manuscript where it pertains to a specific institution. These are: Academy of Natural Sciences of Philadelphia, Donna Umin; Albert Einstein Medical Center — Daroff Division, Myra F. Stayton; Albert Einstein Medical Center — Northern Division, Sandra Thompson; American College of Physicians, Mark Chrismeyer and Stephen T. Donohue; American Philosophical Society Library, Murphy D. Smith, Jr.; Children's Hospital of Philadelphia, Shirley Bonnem; College of Physicians of Philadelphia, William F. Chaveas, Lisabeth M. Holloway and Elizabeth M. Moyer; F. A. Davis Company, Robert H.

Craven; Friends Hospital, David B. Arnold; Hahnemann Medical Center, Marjorie R. Carmosin and Joseph R. DiPalma, M.D.; Hill-Physick-Keith House, Victoria Byrne; Historical Society of Pennsylvania, Joseph P. McLaughlin and Dorothy Hauck; Hospital of the University of Pennsylvania, Marilyn Castaldi and Gerald Katz; Institute of Pennsylvania Hospital, J. Martin Myers, M.D., and Susan Perloff; Lankenau Hospital, Blanche Day and Hudson G. Scattergood; Lea & Febiger, John F. Spahr; Library Company of Philadelphia, Edwin Wolfe, 2nd; J. B. Lippincott Company, Joseph W. Lippincott, Jr.; Medical College of Pennsylvania, Marion S. Fay, Ph.D., Charles A. Glanville and Anne Insinger; Morris Arboretum, Gordon A. Brandes; Naval Regional Medical Center, Lieutenant Dean A. Hermann, MSC, USN; Pennsylvania College of Optometry, Phyllis Propert and Norman E. Wallis, Ph.D., O.D.; Philadelphia College of Pharmacy and Science, John Bergen, Ph.D., Alfonso R. Gennaro, Ph.D., John Hoover, Daniel Hussar, Ph.D., John E. Kramer, Arthur Osol, Ph.D., Louis A. Reber, Ph.D., Joseph A. Solomon, Ph.D., and Linwood F. Tice; Pennsylvania College of Podiatric Medicine, James E. Bates, D.P.M.; Pennsylvania Horticultural Society, Julie L. Morris; Pennsylvania Hospital, Dolores Ziff; Philadelphia Child Guidance Clinic, Philip H. Wagner; Philadelphia College of Osteopathic Medicine, Margaret F. Ferguson, Sherwood R. Mercer and Thomas M. Rowland, Jr.; Philadelphia County Medical Society, Donald C. Geist, M.D.; Philadelphia General Hospital, Elaine E. Madden; St. Agnes Hospital, Sister Anthony Consilia; W. B. Saunders Company, John L. Dusseau; Temple University Health Sciences Center, Robert A. Holland; Thomas Jefferson University, H. Bruce Ewart; United States Naval Home, Rear Admiral C. J. Van Arsdall, USN; University of Pennsylvania, Trudy King and Donald T. Sheehan; Wills Eye Hospital, Ruth J. Armour; and the Wistar Institute of Anatomy and Biology, Margaret P. O'Neill.

And, finally, I am especially grateful to Doris P. Shalley, whose unerring eye was invaluable in checking each detail of the manuscript.

INTRODUCTION

L ike any other profession or scientific discipline, the practice of
medicine in the United States had to have a beginning somewhere
in the country. But no historian can safely set the place or the time. Yet it is
far from presumptuous to say that its practice on a significant scale began
in Philadelphia earlier than elsewhere in the Colonies. There were undoubtedly doctors on Roanoke Island, in Jamestown or at Plimoth Plan-
tation; and certainly there was disease in these early settlements, but there
does not appear to have been any extensive or organized practice of medicine before its blossoming in Philadelphia.

Philadelphia enjoys the distinction of possessing "the first and the
oldest" of many health care institutions, and might in good faith, therefore,
legitimately lay claim to being the birthplace of medicine in America. If other
towns and cities dispute this view—and some undoubtedly will—few can
deny that in Philadelphia medicine received an early and notable impetus.

From its earliest days, Philadelphia has been examined, explored
and analyzed by a succession of scholars, writers, journalists and travelers.
Many extolled its virtues (and mentioned some of its sins!), but none denied
its people's enlightenment, their passionate pursuit of all knowledge and
their concern with bettering the human condition.

There were doctors in the time of William Penn, among them two
Quakers, Thomas Wynne and Griffith Owen, about whom little is remembered. Dr. John Kearsley, who first came to Philadelphia in 1711, has been
called "the founder of the medical profession in Philadelphia, marking out
the lines of its future development, and devoting his talents without stint
in many fields of public endeavor."

In little more than a half-century from the time of Dr. Kearsley's
arrival, the medical school of the University of Pennsylvania was established
(1765). This act alone seemed to give the city the momentum it needed to
make medicine one of the foremost of all Philadelphia's many bequests to
the nation.

If we consider the Philadelphia institutions that are well over 150 or
200 years in age, the list is impressive. The Almshouse (now Philadelphia
General Hospital) was established in 1729, Pennsylvania Hospital in 1751,
the College of Physicians of Philadelphia in 1787, Friends Hospital in 1813,
the Philadelphia College of Pharmacy and Science in 1821, and Jefferson
Medical College (now part of Thomas Jefferson University) in 1824. No
other American city has such a heritage. Furthermore, these institutions
and others founded soon afterward still play a lively role in the life of Philadelphia at the Bicentennial.

The 19th century was the Golden Age of Philadelphia medicine. The
men who wielded the scalpel or taught in the surgical amphitheatre, at the

bedside or in the classroom or pondered the mysteries of mind, body and medicine in the study—these were joined by the heroes of the laboratory. The great drama of medicine in Philadelphia in the 19th century was enacted in parallel fashion in Europe, particularly in France, Germany and Austria. While other American cities produced statesmen, writers, artists and actors, Philadelphia (although it had its share of these) concentrated on producing doctors. Their names form a pantheon of American medicine: Samuel D. Gross, D. Hayes Agnew, the William Peppers (father and son), Sir William Osler and S. Weir Mitchell, to mention only a few.

It should never be forgotten by the visitor or the citizen of Philadelphia that to be associated with medicine in this city was in the past a supreme achievement, the highest possible dignity. The Philadelphia doctor was, and is, a person highly venerated by the community.

To write the story of Philadelphia medicine in all its complexity and drama was never the object of this book. Such an undertaking would require many years and perhaps should never be attempted in one volume. In the individual stories of Philadelphia institutions and the men and women who made them great, we can see the magnificent saga of Philadelphia medicine in an intimate way. A comprehensive history might minimize the human element.

Philadelphia Medica is in some ways a prismatic view of the subject. It is a guide that attempts to give the visitor a view of Philadelphia from a different perspective. It gives the histories of health institutions, presents the medical *dramatis personae* (whether on center stage or in the wings) and captures intimate personal glimpses of the many Philadelphians who have helped to establish the city's reputation for leadership in the health sciences.

In any book of this size and scope, there must be certain limits. This guide is chiefly concerned with the buildings that are historically the oldest and the institutions that were the first of their kind. Because every health institution in Philadelphia could not be included, only those that are of interest historically, or that by their uniqueness could be expected to arouse the special interest of visitors to the city, have been written up in full; many others, however, have been given brief mention. The teaching institutions— the colleges of medicine, pharmacy, veterinary medicine, dentistry, optometry and podiatric medicine—have been included because of their national and international repute.

Any quest is certain to be exciting, and none has been more so for the author than this exploration of the medical and health history of Philadelphia. Welcome to Philadelphia and the pleasures of Philadelphia medica. May your discovery of them be as satisfying as mine has been.

John Francis Marion

Philadelphia 1976

I THE OLD CITY

For the purposes of this book, the City of Philadelphia has been divided into arbitrary geographical sections. This one, called "The Old City," follows the plan of William Penn's "Greene Countrie Towne," except that instead of including all the area on Thomas Holme's map of 1683, "The Old City" extends only from the Delaware River to Broad Street, rather than to the Schuylkill River. We are concerned here with the 14 city blocks from the river to the east side of Broad Street and with that part of the city extending from Race Street and Franklin Square on the north to Pine Street on the south. Thus, our Old City is the Old City, but with certain liberties taken.

Independence Hall
Chestnut Street between Fifth and Sixth Streets

The focus on America's most revered shrine during the Bicentennial is mainly concerned with the events of state that took place behind its walls. However, there were also events of a medical nature within the State House (as it was originally called), but these tend to be forgotten in the rush of those concerned with life, liberty and the pursuit of happiness.

We know that late in 1743 Dr. Adam Spencer, Edinburgh-trained, came from Boston to Philadelphia. He has been described "as a most Judicious and experienced Physician and Man-midwife." While here, Dr. Spencer delivered a series of lectures at the State House, and in his *Autobiography*, Benjamin Franklin speaks of his indebtedness to Spencer for the knowledge of electricity he received at these lectures. On May 29, 1744, Dr. Spencer lectured on the eye, his purpose being "to account for the Faculties, the Nature and Diseases of that Instrument of Sight." This was one of the earliest public medical lectures held in Philadelphia, and it was certainly one of the first scientific discussions of ophthalmology. Charlatans, quacks and posturers often treated the eye with damaging results in 18th century America. Spencer was also the first doctor to attempt, without much success, to "challenge the monopoly exercised by the city's midwives."

When the Pennsylvania Hospital was being organized, we learn that the State House was again used as a place of public meeting. A meeting of the contributors to the hospital was held there on July 1, 1751, when 12 managers and a treasurer were chosen to serve until the "first second day in the Month called May." Among those chosen as managers that day was Benjamin Franklin, who was also selected to be clerk.

A portrait by Benjamin West of James Hamilton, Lieutenant-Governor of the Province, hangs in the Long Gallery on the second floor. (The room was used as a hospital for soldiers of the Continental army after the Battle of Germantown.) The board of managers of Pennsylvania Hospital sought Hamilton's help in securing for the hospital a suitable tract of land from Thomas and Richard Penn, the proprietors. Although Hamilton had approved the Charter (granted by the Assembly) on May 11, 1751, it seems he was not in favor of the project and cautioned the Penns against granting the request of the managers.

Much later, in 1765, Dr. William Shippen, Jr., gave his introductory anatomical lecture (first of a series of public lectures) in Independence Hall, prior to the opening of the medical school of the College of Philadelphia (later the University of Pennsylvania). In delivering the lectures on anatomy, Dr. Shippen used the magnificent anatomical drawings by Jan van Rymsdyck that Dr. John Fothergill presented to Pennsylvania Hospital in 1762. They can still be seen at the hospital in the old library.

But these happenings were only a prelude to the greatest event of all, the signing of the Declaration of Independence on July 4, 1776. On this historic occasion, which has had its impact on all the democracies of the 19th and 20th centuries, an especially well-known Philadelphia physician, Dr. Benjamin Rush, added his name to the declaration of freedom from the Mother Country. The inkwell used, which can be seen in the Assembly Room today, was made by the distinguished Philadelphia silversmith Philip Syng, whose grandson was the equally famous Dr. Philip Syng Physick.

There was also a doctor who lay in state in Independence Hall, a singular honor. The biers of Abraham Lincoln, Henry Clay and John Quincy Adams received public viewing here, and so did that of Elisha Kent Kane, M.D. (1820-1857). This physician, naval officer and pioneer explorer of the American route to the North Pole, studied at the medical school of the University of Pennsylvania and was elected a resident physician at the Pennsylvania Hospital when he was only 20 and still an undergraduate. After graduating in medicine from the university in 1842, he became a surgeon in the United States Navy and toured India, the Philippines, the Dutch East Indies and Egypt.

His spirit of adventure led him to join the First Grinnell Expedition (1850) to the Arctic in search of the missing explorer Sir John Franklin, who was lost in 1845 while seeking the Northwest Passage. Thus stimulated, he headed the Second Grinnell Expedition (1853-1855), his heroic efforts in the frozen wastes gaining him the admiration of his fellow citizens and of those who accompanied him. The book he wrote about this second adventure became a national best seller and brought him instantaneous acclaim.

In search of health—his was shattered by the years in the Arctic—he died in Havana. His body was returned to Philadelphia, but before reaching here it lay in state in New Orleans, Louisville, Columbus and Baltimore. The obsequies were unrivalled—orations in each of the cities, ceremonies and spectacular processions.

When the cortege—not unlike that of Lincoln less than a decade later—reached Philadelphia, the lying-in-state was held in Independence Hall. The First City Troop provided the guard of honor; the ex-governor and other dignitaries were pallbearers. The young man, not yet 40, who had graduated from medical school a scant 15 years before, had become one of America's most famous doctors.

Open daily during 1976, 9:00 to 6:00 in spring, 9:00 to 8:00 in summer. Other times 9:00 to 5:00.

PHILOSOPHICAL HALL
104 South Fifth Street

Like so many Philadelphia landmarks, the history of Philosophical Hall is interwoven with that of the city and its medical personages and institutions. It is the home of the American Philosophical Society, the oldest learned society in America (1743), which was founded by Benjamin Franklin. Philosophical Hall (1789) is the only privately owned building on Independence Square and older than the others, with the exception of Independence Hall.

Franklin's opening words in his founding prospectus were: "A PROPOSAL for Promoting Useful Knowledge among the British Plantations in America." Among the points he stressed in founding the society were: "That at Philadelphia there be always at least seven Members, viz. a Physician, a Botanist, a Mathematician, a Chemist, a Mechanician, a Geographer, and a general Natural Philosopher...." Modeled after the Royal Society of London, it stressed the categories of medicine and anatomy, husbandry and American improvements. Among the early subscribers were the 18th century physicians Barnabus Binney, John Carson, John Foulke, Samuel P. Griffitts, Gerardus Glentworth, Robert Harris, James Hutchinson, John

PHILOSOPHICAL HALL

10

Jones, Adam Kuhn, John Morgan, Thomas Parke, Benjamin Rush and William Shippen, Jr.

The newly formed (1787) College of Physicians held its meetings here from December 10, 1791, until 1845. Seventeen members of the American Philosophical Society were among the founders of the college. While the college used Philosophical Hall as its headquarters, the terrible yellow fever epidemic of 1793 raged throughout the city. Death faced Philadelphians of all stations in life; the city was paralyzed with fear. The Mayor appealed to the Fellows to meet with him—a most unusual request.

Beginning in 1792, the University of Pennsylvania held lectures on Chemistry, Institutes of Medicine and Clinical Cases, Materia Medica and Practice of Physic here. The list of doctors who have been members of the American Philosophical Society represents a hall of fame of American medicine. Those who come readily to mind are D. Hayes Agnew, Thomas Hewson Bache, Thomas Bond, Thomas Cadwalader, Harvey Cushing, J. Mendez Da Costa, Simon Flexner, Thomas Sovereign Gates, Samuel D. Gross, I. Minis Hays, Thomas Tickell Hewson, William Edmonds Horner, Chevalier Jackson and S. Weir Mitchell. Among the memorabilia within is Thomas Sully's copy of the Bass Otis portrait of Dr. Caspar Wistar, Thomas Jefferson's successor as president of the society. Dr. Nathaniel Chapman, another president, also held the same office in the American Medical Association.

Philosophical Hall is not open to the general public, except upon application by letter.

LIBRARY HALL
105 South Fifth Street

T his handsome building houses one of the great scientific and medical collections of the world. It is a reconstruction (1959) of the building originally built in 1789 and 1790 for the Library Company of Philadelphia, which stood on this site until 1887. The American Philosophical Society is "held at Philadelphia for Promoting useful knowledge," and its library (begun in 1769) is proof of this dedication. Containing 150,000 volumes (including bound periodicals) in the area of health sciences, some of the most valuable items are a substantial collection of early American pamphlets (40 on yellow fever) and histories of eugenics and genetics. There are the papers of Benjamin Smith Barton, physician and naturalist, and a diary that Dr. Thomas Hewson Bache, a great-great-grandson of Benjamin Franklin, kept during the Civil War. John Bartram and his son William, early botanists who greatly influenced apothecaries, are represented as well. Among the prominent 18th and 19th century Philadelphia physicians

LIBRARY HALL

whose papers are here are Thomas Parke, William Shippen, Jr., James Hutchinson (who died in the yellow fever epidemic of 1793), John Morgan, Caspar Wistar and John Fothergill, the English Quaker physician who taught many early Philadelphia doctors.

The library has Dr. George Bacon Wood's correspondence relating to *The Dispensatory of the United States of America*, a correspondence of Samuel George Morton on medical practice, and papers of men and women associated with the Rockefeller Institute: Max Bergmann, Rufus Ivory Cole, Simon Flexner and Florence Rena Sabin. The laboratory notes and files of Eugene Lindsay Opie, pathologist, are preserved as are the papers of Francis Peyton Rous, Nobel Prize winner, and Harold Lindsay Amoss. The latter's are from his medical service in the United States Army during 1918 and 1919 and concern immunology, meningitis and poliomyelitis. The papers of Doctors Amoss, Opie and Rous are directly connected with the Rockefeller Institute, too.

The seeker into the past can find Dr. Benjamin Rush's *Commonplace Book*, begun in 1792 and continued until his death in 1813. It was written for his personal edification "without conscious restraint or art." To be sure, medicine occupied a prominent position in it, but philosophy, biography and poetry did as well — a key to the personality of this complex man. A portrait of Dr. Rush by Thomas Sully — one of the society's great paintings — hangs in the library. The prescription book of William Shippen, Jr., covers the period from October 1789 to July 1791. The doctor kept a daily

12

account of his professional visits and prescriptions in this volume. Some of his patients were such distinguished early Americans as George Washington, Thomas Jefferson and General Henry Knox.

To list all the medical treasures would be impossible, but two might be pointed out as examples of those within the library vaults: *Practical Observations on Vaccination* (1802) by Dr. John Redman Coxe, an early advocate of the practice; and *An Account of the Foxglove, and Some of its Medical Uses: With Practical Remarks on Dropsy and Other Diseases* by William Withering, M.D., an early classic work on digitalis. The student, the researcher, the quester after the medical past can find much of it here.

Open Monday to Friday, 9:00 to 5:00.

SURGEONS' HALL
Fifth Street below Chestnut Street

T he site of the building that once stood here is recorded on one of the markers placed in Independence National Historical Park by the National Park Service. In 1792, the University of Pennsylvania adapted a building on this spot for the use of its medical school, the first in the nation. The building housed a chemical laboratory, classroom and sky-lighted anatomical hall, where dissections were done. It was used by the university until 1870 for anatomical and chemical lectures. The Philadelphia Dispensary, instituted in 1786, occupied the site beginning in 1801. Its concept of payment for benefits sounds like present-day hospital insurance: "Every person who should pay one guinea a year could become a contributor, or on paying ten guineas a life-member. The Contributors chose twelve Managers annually from among themselves, and the Managers annually appointed six attending and four consulting physicians and surgeons, a treasurer and an apothecary....In 1807 the Staff recommended to the Board of Managers the appointment of 'Two Medical Gentlemen to Visit all poor patients laboring under disease who may apply for assistance, and that their prescriptions be made up at the Hospital."

The dispensary carried on its work here until 1922. In 1927, it became affiliated with Pennsylvania Hospital.

CARPENTERS' HALL
Chestnut Street between Third and Fourth Streets

C ertainly one of the most historic buildings in the United States, Carpenters' Hall was built between 1770 and 1773 by the

Carpenters' Company of the City and County of Philadelphia, the oldest builders' organization in the nation. It is remembered today chiefly for its role in the Revolution, more especially because it was the scene of the First Continental Congress in September-October, 1774. However, Carpenters' Hall had many associations with the medical and pharmaceutical professions, too. Long before the Revolution, Samuel Rhoads, a member of the Carpenters' Company, was the architect for Pennsylvania Hospital, and it was here in Carpenters' Hall, after the Declaration of Independence, that The Committee of the City and Liberties of Philadelphia "called for a convention to organize a new government for the province." Among the delegates were Benjamin Franklin and Dr. Benjamin Rush.

During the Revolution itself, the first floor of Carpenters' Hall was commandeered as an infirmary for wounded Continental soldiers under the command of General Gates. By 1777, Philadelphia was occupied by the British, after the routs at the Brandywine and Germantown, and the British continued using the hall as a hospital. It was also used to house residents of the city almshouse who had been turned out by the British when they took over that institution for the quartering of British troops.

After the Revolution and well into the first quarter of the 19th century, Carpenters' Hall served in another way to link historic American buildings and the medical profession. It was here, on February 23, 1821, that the Philadelphia College of Pharmacy was organized—the first institution of its kind in the world.

Open daily, 10:00 to 4:00, subject to change.

INTERIOR OF CARPENTERS' HALL

FIRST BANK OF THE UNITED STATES
116 South Third Street

This magnificent building, now restored to its 18th century grandeur, is a monument to the early financial geniuses of the new nation — those men who made the world of finance work. Stephen Girard (1750-1831), merchant, financier, philanthropist, was associated with this building long after he arrived in Philadelphia in the crucial year of 1776.

The first Bank of the United States was here from 1797 to 1811. In 1810, always a supporter of the First United States Bank, Girard served on a committee of five to draw up a memorial petitioning Congress to renew the bank's charter, which was about to expire. When Congress refused and the bank was forced to close its doors, Girard bought the building (1812) and other assets and started the Bank of Stephen Girard as a private venture.

Before this time, during the yellow fever epidemic of 1793, in which over 4,000 persons died between August 1 and November 9, Girard not only gave liberally of his time and money, but with Peter Helm he volunteered to act as superintendent at the fever hospital at Bush Hill. This involved the care of patients and "for sixty days Stephen Girard performed both day and night the duty of receiving, nursing, and caring for those stricken with the fever."

This tells only part of the story, and only in the most skeletal way. Girard, who was then a man of substance in Philadelphia, actually did day-by-day nursing of the most basic kind. He bathed, cleaned and ministered to the sick; he saw to it that they had medication and food. He sat up nights caring for the dying, he tended those whose bedding was soiled and would not have been cleaned otherwise. In fact, this man of the Establishment performed the most menial tasks. This was his contribution to his adopted city and its people in a time of peril, and he did it with good grace and humility. For this, Philadelphia never forgot the French immigrant, blind in one eye, whose wife was incarcerated for many years at Pennsylvania Hospital.

BENJAMIN RUSH HOUSE
Third and Walnut Streets

The charming garden at this site, recently created during the restoration of Independence National Historical Park, marks the location of the home of Benjamin Rush (1746-1813), prominent

Philadelphia physician and one of five doctors to sign the Declaration of Independence. (The others were Josiah Bartlett, Lyman Hall, Matthew Thornton and Oliver Wolcott.) Dr. Rush, often called "the father of American psychiatry," lived here from about 1791 until 1793. He is remembered in Philadelphia for his many contributions to the city: he was named a delegate to the Second Continental Congress in 1776 and was a Signer. His greatest contribution medically was his loyalty to his fellow citizens during the yellow fever epidemic of 1793 when over 4,000 died.

Yellow fever had been prevalent in Philadelphia from its beginnings as a city, and even before. In 1699, it was called the Barbadoes Distemper; in 1741, the Palatinate Distemper; the American Plague in 1754-1755; and the Dutch Distemper in 1787. During the epidemic of 1741, the afflicted were housed in the pesthouse on League Island.

At one time, 20,000 fled the city, yet Dr. Rush stayed on and tended the ill and dying with little help. Today we recall him for his valiant efforts in behalf of the epidemic victims. Rush, who was also called "the American Sydenham," was an early discoverer of the causes of dengue (breakbone fever). He believed the origin of the yellow fever "was from the exhalations of gutters, docks, cellars, common sewers, ponds of stagnant water and from the foul air of the ship [Deborah] formerly mentioned."

The house in which Dr. Rush was born is no longer standing. However, the stones and woodwork are in storage on the grounds of the Philadelphia State Hospital, saved by Robert E. Jones, M.D. The great-grandparents of Benjamin, John and Susanna Rush, arrived in Byberry Township in 1683. The house which was to be the Signer's birthplace was erected about 1690 and continued to be inhabited until 1965. It was razed in 1969. The Pennsylvania Legislature has been asked to allocate funds for the creation of a 275-acre Benjamin Rush State Park on which the house of his birth will be re-erected.

PENNSYLVANIA HORTICULTURAL SOCIETY
325 Walnut Street

Philadelphia, which can claim the oldest medical school in the nation as well as the oldest hospital, also points with pride to the Pennsylvania Horticultural Society, the oldest ongoing horticultural organization in America. Founded in 1827, the society has promoted the beautification of the city by planting trees, has encouraged the development of parks and gardens, and has maintained a splendid and valuable reference library. One of the buildings that housed the society's headquarters was occupied in the 19th century by Dr. William Chandler, an apothecary.

As its contribution to the Bicentennial, the society will mount an exhibition from April to October, 1976, called "From Seed to Flower 1681-1876: A Horticultural Point of View." The exhibit, built around 38 volumes of the 18th and 19th centuries, the great majority from the society's library, will draw attention to contributions of Philadelphians to the horticultural and botanical knowledge of our emerging nation. Of special interest to the medical and pharmaceutical world will be such volumes as *An Inaugural Botanico-Medical Dissertation on the Phytolacca decandra of Linnaeus* by Benjamin Shultz, which was published in this city in 1795 and concerns the pokeberry experiments; *Vegetable Materia Medica of the United States* by William Paul Crillon Barton, published in Philadelphia 1817-1818; Jacob Bigelow's *American Medical Botany*, issued in Boston in the years 1817-1820; and Joseph Carson's *Illustrations of Medical Botany*, which Philadelphians first read in 1847. The society's rare book collection contains many herbals; these can be seen by making special application.

The visitor leaving the exhibit should pause and examine the delights of the 18th century garden maintained by the society. This formal garden, with its geometrical patterns and parterres of flowers, is similar to one an 18th century Philadelphian would have had after he achieved success and position in the colony. There is also a small orchard, and behind the society's headquarters (but not always open to the public) is an area reserved for herbs, vegetables and cutting flowers.

The special exhibit will be open seven days a week from 9:00 to 5:00.

SHIPPEN-WISTAR HOUSE
240 South Fourth Street

One of the finest mansions surviving in this part of the city, the Shippen-Wistar House is not only beautiful but also has medical associations going back to the middle of the 18th century. It was built about 1750 by Dr. William Shippen (1712-1801). We are told: "The elder William Shippen, whose shop was at the Sign of Paracelsus' Head, was one of these [apothecaries]; as his experience and skill increased, his patients became more numerous, and giving up the trade of drug-seller, he rose to the rank of physician." Like so many physicians of his time in Philadelphia, he played an active role in the affairs of the city and was a member of the Continental Congress in 1778 and 1780. In July 1776, he wrote his brother Edward: "I give you joy of the late declaration of Independence."

Dr. William Shippen, Jr. (1736-1808), his son, who studied medicine in Edinburgh and was one of the first members of the faculty of the medical school of the College of Philadelphia (professor of anatomy and surgery),

SHIPPEN-WISTAR HOUSE

lived here and delivered lectures to students who were unable to study medicine abroad. Dr. Shippen, Jr., was a pioneer in numerous ways: he was one of the first to use human bodies for dissection, and in 1765 had to defend himself against the accusation of "body snatching." Medical students and teachers had to find their own cadavers in the 18th century and there was a great traffic in grave robbing. In 1770, a mob became excited over the grave-robbing issue and attacked the Shippen house and broke its windows. Young Dr. Shippen was chief of the medical department of the Army for a time during the Revolution.

The house was sold in 1798 to another Philadelphia physician of note, Dr. Caspar Wistar (1761-1818), who lived here from that time until his death. He too was associated with the University of Pennsylvania, as well as with Pennsylvania Hospital, and was one of the early exponents of vaccination. He also produced the first medical textbook in 1811. It was his custom to hold open house for the members of the American Philosophical Society, which brought to the house doctors and scientists in other fields. These "Wistar Parties" were continued for some years after his death. The wistaria vine, whose clusters so enhance the gardens of old Philadelphia homes, was named for him as was the Wistar Institute, where his examples of brain dissections (circa 1808) formed the nucleus for the present collection.

Among the other mementoes of a medical nature within the house is a portrait of Dr. S. Weir Mitchell (1829-1914) by John Singer Sargent, whose own father was for a time a Philadelphia doctor. The house is now owned by the Mutual Assurance Company for Insuring Houses from Loss by Fire, popularly known as the "Green Tree," which was founded in 1784, making it the second oldest fire insurance company in America.

The house is not open to the public.

HILL-PHYSICK-KEITH HOUSE
321 South Fourth Street

This magnificent house, one of the most beautiful in America, is treasured by architectural historians because it is the only free-standing house in Society Hill and the only Federal house in Philadelphia that has been restored with Federal furniture. What is of interest to us is that Dr. Philip Syng Physick (1768-1837) lived here from 1815 until his death—the house having been given to him by his sister Abigail, who bought it from the original owner Henry Hill (executor of Benjamin Franklin's will).

The home is not only a monument to the architect who designed it, the men who built it, and the cabinetmakers whose genius shows in the furniture within, but it is also a medical shrine to one of the greatest surgeons in America during his lifetime, the originator of many bold operative procedures and the inventor of a number of instruments. He devised a flexible catheter, removed cataracts, did plastic repair of harelip, and was the first to use a pump to wash out the contents of the stomach after the ingestion of poison. We do know that in 1812, by employing the stomach pump, he saved the life of a black child who had swallowed laudanum.

The most famous operation Dr. Physick was to perform took place in 1831 in this house when the doctor removed a stone from the bladder of Chief Justice John Marshall, then in his 76th year. The doctor himself was then 63 years old. It must be remembered that this was before the introduction of anesthesia, but the venerable Virginian survived to present Dr. Physick with a handsome silver wine cooler in appreciation. It can be seen in the small study, or the green room as it is often called, to the left of the entrance hall. Above it hangs a portrait of the Chief Justice. The actual stone removed from Marshall can still be seen in the Mütter Museum at the College of Physicians. Ironically, Marshall died in Philadelphia four years later when he came to consult Dr. Physick about a disease of the liver. Even the doctor's skill could not save the octogenarian. It was following Marshall's death that the Liberty Bell cracked while tolling for his funeral procession.

The wine cooler is not the only gift from a noted patient that is preserved here. The romantic painting of the Roman ruins in the drawing room was given to the doctor by a grateful Joseph Bonaparte, the exiled King of Spain, who lived in Philadelphia for a number of years. In the

19

dining room is a silver pitcher that Commodore James Barron, who killed Stephen Decatur in a duel, also gave Dr. Physick. It bears the couplet:

The offer of feeling to the Surgeon who feels
As much pleasure in healing as he whom he heals.

Dr. Physick invented a miniature guillotine for the removal of the tonsils and introduced the use of catgut ligatures, instead of silk or flax threads, to tie blood vessels. He was also eminently successful in setting broken bones. In 1820, he introduced a method of treating ununited fractures, which was a remarkable improvement on the older methods of treating this condition. At that time, when a bone failed to unite, the patient would be left with what was referred to as a "flail limb," a useless arm or leg. Dr. Physick introduced a seton, a sort of thick thread of twisted silk or muslin, which acted as a foreign body and caused inflammation of the ends of the bone. A callous was formed by the inflammatory secretion, thus uniting the edges of the bone. This and other great steps forward in surgery carried his name and reputation well beyond the limits of Philadelphia. Toward the end of his life, his fees amounted to $20,000 a year, and he was worth a half-million dollars at his death.

Dr. Physick lived well, as befitted a physician of his standing. The house has been beautifully restored by the Annenberg Foundation and then presented to the Philadelphia Society for the Preservation of Landmarks. A portrait of Dr. Physick by Henry Inman presides over the drawing

INTERIOR OF HILL-PHYSICK-KEITH HOUSE

room, and his bust in terra-cotta can be seen at the Pennsylvania Academy of the Fine Arts.

In an upstairs room is an extraordinary collection of instruments used by Dr. Jacob Randolph, Physick's son-in-law, who was also on the staff of Pennsylvania Hospital. They were made in Paris by F. Charrière, to be carried in a case (here also) with a recessed handle and brass inlay. Nearby in the display case is an account from the *Philadelphia Gazette*, November 6, 1836, stating that Dr. Randolph used the instruments—which he exhibited before the operation—for the "removal of a large calculus from a living patient." He was the first in Philadelphia to perform lithotrity, the crushing of a stone within the bladder. There is also a medicine chest (circa 1820) with the original hand-blown bottles and flat stoppers. It has a "secret drawer," with one key to open both the drawer and the chest. There are books belonging to Dr. John Syng Dorsey, Dr. Physick's nephew, and an engraving of him that "was caused to be ENGRAVED by his PRIVATE PUPILS." This room was always kept ready for Dr. Dorsey when he was on duty at Pennsylvania Hospital.

The house is open to the public Tuesday-Saturday, 10:00-4:00; Sunday, 1:00-4:00. Admission $2.00.

OLD PINE PRESBYTERIAN CHURCH
Fourth and Pine Streets

J ust a short stroll from the Hill-Physick-Keith House is the Third Presbyterian Church (popularly known as "Old Pine"), "the only Presbyterian Church still within the boundaries of the Old City of Philadelphia and dating back to before the Revolution." Built in 1768, it was rebuilt in 1837 (when the Greek Revival front was added) and in 1857.

We know that two colonial physicians, Benjamin Rush and William Shippen, Jr., the latter onetime Director-General of Hospital for the Continental army, worshipped here. Dr. Shippen also served as a trustee. During the British occupation of Philadelphia (1777), the troops tore out the pews for firewood and the dragoons stabled their horses here. Later the church was used as a hospital.

In the 19th century Ezra Stiles Ely, minister from 1814 to 1835, was a generous benefactor of Jefferson Hospital.

21

MOTHER BETHEL AFRICAN METHODIST EPISCOPAL CHURCH

Sixth and Addison Streets

T he ground on which this church (the fourth building on this site) stands is the oldest piece of property owned by black people in the United States. Its origins have a connection with Philadelphia medicine because of Bishop Richard Allen (1760-1831), a slave who had been given a license to preach in 1784 and had bought his freedom two years later. He and his followers were allowed to hold services at five o'clock in the morning on Sundays at Saint George's Methodist Church on North Fourth Street. The day came when they were told they could no longer do so, but must use the balcony. Allen, who was later ordained bishop by a bishop of the Methodist Episcopal Church in Philadelphia, led his flock from the church and purchased this ground. He was helped morally and financially by Dr. Benjamin Rush in gratitude for his assistance during the yellow fever epidemic of 1793, when thousands fled the city and those remaining were afraid to help with the sick. Bishop Allen came to Rush's aid and ministered to the sick and dying, thereby earning the gratitude of Dr. Rush and his fellow citizens.

WASHINGTON SQUARE

Walnut Street between Sixth and Seventh Streets

W ashington Square, in certain ways the most beautiful of the city's original five squares, has medical associations going back to its beginning. Medicine concerns itself with preserving and pro-longing life, but it is also concerned with death. And so was Washington Square. It was planned when Charles II was on the throne and is shown on Thomas Holme's 1683 map of Philadelphia. During the reign of Queen Anne, we find the city had requested "some convenient burying place for all strangers or others who might not so conveniently be laid in any of particular enclosures appropriated by certain religious societies for that purpose." This led William Penn's four commissioners on January 20, 1706, to sign a patent designating the Southeast Square (as it was then called) as a Potter's Field. It has been estimated that some three thousand bodies were buried in Washington Square, at least two thousand of these British and American soldiers during the Revolution. Others were Acadians, who were deported from Nova Scotia by the British during the French and Indian

War; the victims of the yellow fever epidemic of 1793; and prisoners from the Walnut Street Prison and the nearby Debtor's Prison.

There are other medical associations, too. About the year 1805, the Committee of City Councils refused permission to the University of Pennsylvania to erect a building on the square for the use of its medical school. And Jefferson Medical College spent some of its formative years on Locust Street in the Tivoli Theatre (also known as the Prune Street Theatre), which could be seen from the square.

The trees are larger and older than those of the other city squares and there is a special dignity to this "six acres, three roods and three perches." Dignity lent enchantment and helped lure commercial establishments to the square. Long the heart of the local publishing scene, today three of the four medical publishing houses of Philadelphia—Lea & Febiger, J. B. Lippincott Company, and W. B. Saunders Company—have their offices facing this burial ground-cum-city park.

Philadelphia never forgets its animals, and veterinarians are invariably pleased to see the old horse drinking troughs such as the one on the south side, nearby Lea & Febiger's offices. It bears an appropriate (if free) inscription from Proverbs:

Let Thy Fountain Be
Dispersed Broad
And Rivers of Water in
The Streets

The thoughtful donors designed it on three levels so that dogs, cats and the many birds in the square could also quench their thirst.

WASHINGTON SQUARE

LEA & FEBIGER

South Washington Square

The Florentine palazzo, designed by E. Nelson Edwards and built in 1923-1924, houses the offices of the oldest publishing house in the United States (1785), which is also the oldest medical publisher. Even more remarkable is the fact that Francis Carey Lea, Jr., one of the current partners, is a great-great-great grandson of Mathew Carey (1760-1839), the founder of the firm.

Carey, a Dublin firebrand, published near-seditious writings—pamphlets and newspapers—and was forced to leave Ireland on two occasions. On the first, he fled to Paris, where he met Benjamin Franklin and worked with him at his press in Passy. It was there, too, that he was introduced to the Marquis de Lafayette. After his return to Ireland, Carey was even more unwelcome because of the increasingly inflammatory nature of his writings. This time he emigrated to Philadelphia, arriving here in November, 1784, with only a few guineas in his pocket. Lafayette, who was then in America, heard of his plight and sent him a check for four hundred dollars. With this, Carey established a daily journal and soon after began publishing books and pamphlets. Carey repaid his debt to Lafayette 40 years later when the aged marquis, then in straitened circumstances, made a triumphal return to the land he helped liberate.

Medical books made their appearance on Carey's list from the earliest days, the first (1792) being a pamphlet on rabies dedicated to Dr. Benjamin Rush and a treatise on the care of infants. Carey stayed in Philadelphia during the yellow fever epidemic of 1793 and wrote a dramatic account of it that went through four editions in three months and sold 10,000 copies. Some months later, he was the publisher of Dr. Rush's own account of the same calamitous time.

By 1794, he was able to advertise a list of books which included 11 medical texts, and in 1820 he founded the *Philadelphia Journal of the Medical and Physical Sciences*, a quarterly periodical edited by Dr. Nathaniel Chapman (later to be the first president of the American Medical Association) with whom were subsequently associated Drs. William P. Dewees, John D. Godman and Isaac Hays. In 1827, the sphere of the publication was enlarged from a local to a national journal of the profession and the name was changed to *The American Journal of the Medical Sciences*. One of Carey's employees was Presley Blakiston, who founded the Blakiston Company (1843), a Philadelphia medical publisher since absorbed by Doubleday and Company and now owned by McGraw-Hill Company.

As the firm expanded (it was now Carey & Lea), more medical books were printed, and in 1830 some 18 medical titles were to be found on a list

LEA & FEBIGER

of 67 titles; by 1845 there were nearly 60. In the decade of the 1840's Lea & Blanchard (Lea was Carey's son-in-law) became predominantly a medical house. Since 1859, the firm has been the publisher of the American edition of *Gray's Anatomy*, the most famous work in all medical literature, often termed "The Bible of Medicine." It is constantly revised by the most able minds of the medical profession.

J.B. LIPPINCOTT COMPANY
227 South Sixth Street

Often thought of as Dickensian by its authors, and one of the oldest publishing houses in the United States, J. B. Lippincott Company has been a leading medical publisher for well over a century. *The Dispensatory of the United States of America* has been published by the firm since 1833, the 27th edition appearing in 1973, making it the oldest continuously published reference work under private ownership in the world. The latest edition was published as *The United States Dispensatory*, the name it was popularly known by for years.

During the Civil War, it was said that there were not one hundred men in America with any in-depth knowledge of surgery and not a thousand men had even seen an operation. Dr. Samuel D. Gross, the surgeon who brought honor to Jefferson Medical College and Hospital, wrote A *Manual of Military Surgery*, which Lippincott published in an edition of 2,000 copies. It soon became evident that this number would not be enough to supply the demand, so a second printing was ordered. The Confederates used it, too, printing it in Richmond with a disclaimer: "Conditions beyond our control prevent us from making the usual reprint arrangements." It was said that many doctors who used the manual, never having performed an operation, would simply open the book, read the directions, and begin to operate in the field.

Earlier, in 1857, the company launched *The Medico-Chirurgical Review* under the editorship of Dr. Gross, but publication was suspended in 1861 due to the Civil War. Dr. D. Hayes Agnew was the author of the three-volume *Treatise on the Principles and Practice of Surgery*, and in 1870 a new periodical, *Medical Times*, was published for the first time. *Annals of Surgery* appeared under the Lippincott imprint in 1897 and continues to do so today, the oldest exclusively surgical journal in the world. *International Clinics*, a quarterly journal for the general practitioner, was begun in 1891 and continued until 1946. At the present time, the company publishes 20 major medical periodicals, a number of these for medical societies.

W. B. SAUNDERS COMPANY
West Washington Square

On the west side of the square, on the corner of Locust Street, facing its competitors and the memorial to the Unknown Soldiers of the Revolution, stands the home of the youngest of the medical publishers that flank three sides of Washington Square. The present building has been its headquarters since 1912. Twenty-four years earlier, Walter Burns Saunders entered medical publishing in a modest way. Today the firm is the world's largest in the health science field.

The first offices were at 33 South 10th Street, a location chosen because of its nearness to Jefferson Medical College and Hospital. Saunders showed his astuteness in this move, because many of his early authors were on the staff at Jefferson. He was wise also in laying down three principles for his fledgling firm: his authors must be leaders and authorities who were actually engaged in the disciplines about which they wrote; books must be produced as finely as possible; and prompt service must be maintained in getting the books to the customers. That these tenets paid off is evidenced by the company's success.

Some of the early and distinguished titles were *Surgery* by J. Chalmers

Da Costa, *Diseases of the Eye* by George E. de Schweinitz and E. B. Gleason's *Nose, Throat and Ear.* By 1891, business was expanding and a move was made to 913 Walnut Street, followed by another to 925 in 1893. This last address had special medical memories, for it was here that the elder Chevalier Jackson occupied the garret during his student days at Jefferson.

Two early successes at this time were the *American Textbook of Surgery* by W. W. Keen of Jefferson Medical College and J. William White of the University of Pennsylvania, which sold 40,000 copies, and *Practice of Medicine* by William Pepper of the University of Pennsylvania (his statue stands on the 33rd Street side of the University Museum, facing the University Hospital), one of the outstanding teachers and practitioners in America at that time.

In 1890, the *American Illustrated Dictionary* (now *Dorland's Illustrated Medical Dictionary*), attributed to W. Newman Dorland, was first published. It is undoubtedly the most widely used medical book ever published. What is not generally known is that a Saunders editor, Ryland W. Greene, was the actual author of the book — a memorable act of ghost-writing. By 1907, the firm had expanded its list even further and entered the field of nursing education textbooks, beginning with only three titles. The present list has approximately 90 titles in this category.

Other milestones in medical publishing that made their appearance in the years following the turn of the century were Keen's *Surgery* in nine volumes. It was in this work that Dr. Keen first revealed that an operation on Grover Cleveland's jaw had taken place in 1893. After the President's death in 1908, there was no longer any reason for secrecy.

Saunders has the distinction of having first published Sigmund Freud in English. The Viennese psychoanalyst was a contributor on neurology to the 1903 translation of *Nothnagel's Encyclopedia* (in 15 volumes).

In 1968, following the death of Lawrence Saunders, chairman of the board, the company was acquired by the Columbia Broadcasting System, Inc., ending 80 years of independent operation and ownership by the Saunders family. However, the name and the reputation for fine medical books that Walter Burns Saunders laid down in 1888 endures as the company approaches its centenary.

MUSICAL FUND HALL
808 Locust Street

While this building is renowned because it was originally designed by William Strickland (1788-1854), the architect responsible for some of Philadelphia's most beautiful and distinctive buildings (it was later altered on two occasions by other architects), we remember it because of one of the most dramatic moments in medical education in the United States. On December 30, 1851, when The Female Medical College of Pennsylvania (now The Medical College of Pennsylvania) held its first graduation here, awarding M.D. degrees to women, the action was so controversial that 500 male medical students and their friends protested the ceremonies and threatened to interrupt them. The Mayor of Philadelphia assigned 50 policemen to cordon off Musical Fund Hall so that order could be maintained. Eight intrepid and dedicated young women received their degrees. Among them were Drs. Phoebe Way and Anna Mary Longshore, who set up practice in Philadelphia's outlying area, and Dr. Hannah Longshore, who became the first woman to hang out her shingle and have a private practice in Philadelphia—three brave young women in light of the outcry their graduation precipitated.

Another partisan of freedom and liberty—Abraham Lincoln—failed to receive the necessary number of votes for the vice presidential nomination when the first Republican National Convention held its sessions here in June 1856. Musical as well as medical and political history was made here, too. Jenny Lind, Adelina Patti and other musical immortals performed here, but we recall with the greatest pride the eight remarkable women who, over a century ago, made medical history here.

PENNSYLVANIA HOSPITAL
Spruce and Pine Streets between Eighth and Ninth Streets

Perhaps no hospital in Philadelphia has so captured the city's imagination as has Pennsylvania Hospital because it is the oldest in the city and its architecture is certainly the most beautiful. The 18th and early 19th century buildings facing the garden on Pine Street are peerless in their beauty. What is even more remarkable is that they have been in constant use since they were erected: the East Wing in 1755; the West Wing in 1796; the Center House in 1804.

Founded by Benjamin Franklin and Dr. Thomas Bond in 1751, Pennsylvania Hospital is the oldest hospital in the United States in the modern sense of the term and is the nation's first voluntary hospital. When Dr. Bond first disclosed his plan for the hospital, the idea received a rather lukewarm reception from the citizenry. He then appealed to Philadelphia's most prominent citizen—Franklin—who had his finger in every pie. The hospital was to relieve "the distress of such distemper'd Poor as from Time to Time came to Philadelphia" and was "for the relief of the sick poor and for the reception and cure of lunaticks." That early premise has always been adhered to. Pennsylvania Hospital has maintained a strong bond with the

PENNSYLVANIA HOSPITAL

community and has the reputation of never turning away anyone from its doors.

The care of the mentally ill was one of the hospital's early concerns. When the East Wing was built in 1755 (the three original hospital buildings were designed by Samuel Rhoads, a member of the board of managers of the hospital as well as of the Carpenters' Company), men were housed on the first floor, women on the second, staff on the third and the "lunaticks" in the basement. The mental cases comprised about one-third of the total caseload at that time. Conditions were humane and advanced for the 18th century: cells were clean, dry and well ventilated; a corridor down the middle provided an exercise area; there were latrines and bathing facilities.

Dr. Benjamin Rush, a staff member, has been described as being "well in advance of his time in regarding insanity as a form of disease rather than a divine visitation." It was he who advocated an early form of occupational therapy, requesting that spinning wheels and wool be provided for the patients.

Two of the patients in the early years provided drama, one physically, the other by her name and presence. Thomas Perrine, described as "a remarkably neat and tidy sailor," was admitted to a cell in 1765, but managed to escape. It appears that he did not want to leave the hospital, but only his cell. He lodged himself in the cupola of the East Wing, and all efforts to remove him were unsuccessful. When the authorities realized Thomas was not going to return to his cell, bedding was provided for him in the cupola

29

and his meals were served to him there. He remained in his eyrie for nine years, until his death in 1774, insensible to the vagaries of weather: the cold, the rain, the heat.

Another patient (committed in 1790) was Mary Lum, wife of Stephen Girard, the merchant prince. Soon after she arrived, it was discovered that she was in a late stage of pregnancy, and although it was contrary to the hospital's policy, she continued as a patient at her husband's request. The child, born in 1791, lived only five months, and it is thought she may have been buried in the hospital grounds. Mary Girard never recovered her reason and lived on until 1815. At Girard's request, she was buried in the hospital's garden. For its care of his wife and child, Girard remembered the hospital handsomely in his will.

The hospital has cared for the sick and wounded of all wars, from the French and Indian War to those of our day. During the occupation of Philadelphia, the British under General Howe deposited the sick and wounded here in such numbers that the managers were forced to ask Howe to desist. Indians also found treatment and care, as did the Acadians, following their expulsion from Nova Scotia during the French and Indian War.

For many years, there was no resident medical officer in the hospital except the apothecary or an apprentice whose indenture to the hospital read that he was "to learn the Art, Trade and Mystery, of an Apothecare." In 1752, Jonathan Roberts was appointed Apothecary to the hospital, to be succeeded by John Morgan, later one of the founders of the medical school of the University of Pennsylvania. (There has always been a close affiliation between Pennsylvania Hospital and the university's medical school; many of the doctors from Pennsylvania Hospital lectured at the school.)

Morgan was a pupil of Dr. John Redman, one of the city's noted doctors; this apprentice-preceptor system was then the accepted mode of learning medicine. The staff from the beginning lent the Apothecary the greatest support. In 1767, they suggested: "...we think a small Laboratory wou'd be of singular use; as such an Apothecary wou'd have a considerable share of leisure, and might prepare most of the chemicals, and the botanical Medicines, avoiding any temptation to adulterate; and we should have many of them, cheaper, genuine, fresh and possessed of their full virtues." An unusual duty of the Apothecary was to keep a daily record of weather conditions, and this practice was continued until the early years of the 20th century. By 1768, an "Elaboratory" had been built which was later leased to the medical department of the Continental army for the preparation of drugs and medical supplies used in the army hospitals.

The hospital had the first outpatient service in the nation and was a pioneer in giving treatment to all races. We have seen that Indians were treated here (as were their victims). Brissot de Warville, who later lost his head during the French Revolution, reported in 1788: "Blacks were here mingled with the whites and lodged in the same apartments. This to me seemed a balm to my soul. I saw a negro woman spinning with activity by the side of her bed."

One of the unusual features of the hospital is its operating theatre —the oldest existing medical amphitheatre in North America (1804). The light from the dome above this circular room provided natural illumination for operating before the days of gas and electricity. It served as a model for the amphitheatre in Massachusetts General Hospital, where ether was first successfully used in surgery. Soon after that event, Dr. James Darrach and Dr. George W. Norris used ether at Pennsylvania Hospital. Even before the operating theatre was built, lectures, dissections and autopsies were conducted at Pennsylvania Hospital. Much earlier, Dr. Thomas Bond had "opened the body before his students, and pointed out the lessons to be derived—'the surest method of obtaining just ideas of diseases.'" In the new amphitheatre in 1805—again before the era of anesthesia—Dr. Physick removed a tumor from the side of a man's face. Drawings were made to show the patient before and after the operation, and we are told the tumor weighed seven pounds.

Much later, in 1887, the first operation deliberately undertaken for the removal of a diseased appendix (in the absence of an emergency) was performed by Dr. Thomas G. Morton. Other doctors concentrated on special areas of research: J. C. Otto on hemophilia; John Kearsley Mitchell on the origins of malarious fever; William Wood Gerhard on the differentiation of typhoid from typhus. In 1911, Dr. R. G. LeConte performed the first thoracoplasty (removal of ribs to permit the collapse of a tubercular lung) in the United States.

Although many Philadelphia hospitals have museums and collections that are noteworthy, Pennsylvania Hospital's is in some ways the most impressive. The historical library houses the oldest collection of medical books in the United States, as well as a notable collection of herbals and horticultural volumes. The long windows face the old garden on Pine Street from the second floor of the Center House. Richly paneled walls, with floor-to-ceiling bookcases and a gallery running around three sides of the room, provide the setting for this priceless collection. Paintings by Benjamin West and the great collection of van Rymsdyk drawings that William Shippen, Jr., used in his first anatomical lecture at Independence Hall may be found in this room. One can also see a chair from William Penn's home at Pennsbury and a cradle said to have been used for Mary Girard's baby. The hospital collection includes one of the rare, beautiful and priceless clocks made by David Rittenhouse, the 18th century clockmaker and astronomer. Two fine portraits by Thomas Sully—of Dr. Benjamin Rush and Samuel Coates—also hang here. Most valuable of all is the American artist Benjamin West's second painting of "Christ Healing the Sick," which the hospital acquired in 1817. The first version, which the artist had promised Pennsylvania Hospital, became so popular in England that it remained there. This second painting was once exhibited on the hospital grounds, and Philadelphians by the hundreds, along with others, came to see it.

A "physic garden," partly filled with medicinal herbs, was planted in the southwest corner of the grounds near Ninth and Pine Streets in 1975. The physicians and surgeons had such a garden in mind in 1769, but its practicality was debated as well as whether it should be on the grounds or elsewhere. Fifty feet wide and circular in design, the garden features plants used medicinally in the 18th century.

Tours of Pennsylvania Hospital can be arranged by calling (215) 829-3251.

THOMAS JEFFERSON UNIVERSITY
Chestnut to Locust Streets between Ninth and Eleventh Streets

The contemporary well-designed buildings in the heart of the city belie the fact that this university houses the city's second oldest medical college. When Jefferson was founded in 1824, neither Paris nor London had two medical schools. Founded by Dr. George McClellan, whose son General George McClellan was to distinguish himself in the Civil War, the school had a complicated origin.

Dr. McClellan, a graduate of the medical school of the University of Pennsylvania, gave lectures in Canonsburg, Pennsylvania, then the home of Jefferson College (now Washington and Jefferson University). On June 1, 1824, young Dr. McClellan began teaching at Walnut and Swanick Streets, just below the present campus of the school, at the site of the former Curtis Publishing Company building. The first year's classes were conducted at the Apollodorian Gallery, but larger quarters were soon needed, and he found more commodious ones in the Tivoli Theatre, 518-20 Locust Street, just opposite the present J. B. Lippincott Company building.

This location, because there were the burying ground of the Fighting Quakers to one side, Potter's Field on another, the Walnut Street Prison and the Debtor's Prison on others, and a friendly tavern nearby, caused Dr. Washington L. Attlee to comment: "Death to the right and left of us, crime and punishment opposite and, thank God, consolation to the rear."

A deputation from the University of Pennsylvania (the nation's *first* medical school) traveled to Harrisburg to inform the Legislature that Dr. McClellan's school had no authority to award M.D. degrees, but was only a branch of Jefferson College. Thus began a rivalry between the two schools that continued for some years, but was replaced in time by the great cordiality and rapport that exist today. But at that time, the Pennsylvania delegation declared that Philadelphia was unable to support two medical colleges—that even New York had tried to do so and had failed. Interestingly enough, although the University of Pennsylvania had the largest enrollment then, within two decades Jefferson's was larger. Between the two, they educated one in every four doctors in the United States during the 19th century.

Although the present university derived its name from the early association with Canonsburg and Jefferson College, there are Thomas Jefferson connections as well. Dr. Robley Dunglison, who had been brought over from England originally to teach at the University of Virginia Medical School, was President Thomas Jefferson's friend and personal physician, and was present at his deathbed in 1826. He was also a member of the staff of Dr. McClellan's new medical school and was, in a way, the second founder of Thomas Jefferson University. He later became the peacemaker between the two medical schools—Jefferson and Pennsylvania.

The early years are of interest because of important connections with distinguished Americans of the 18th century—the Colonial and Revolutionary periods. One of the sons of Robert Morris—often called "the financier of the American Revolution"—graduated from Jefferson. Dr. Franklin Bache, a great-grandson of Benjamin Franklin, was professor of chemistry at Jefferson in 1841 as a member of the "Famous Faculty of

THOMAS JEFFERSON UNIVERSITY

33

'41." He had earlier (1824-1826) been professor of chemistry at the Philadelphia College of Pharmacy and collaborated with his opposite number at the University of Pennsylvania, Dr. George B. Wood, in compiling *The Dispensatory of the United States of America* and *The United States Pharmacopoeia*. Much later, Dr. Fielding O. Lewis, a collateral descendant of George Washington, became professor of otolaryngology.

Although these formative years were important for the new medical college, it was not until the arrival of Dr. Samuel D. Gross, class of 1828, that Jefferson welcomed to its faculty a physician who would be world renowned. Dr. Gross was a native of Easton, Pennsylvania. His statue, by Alexander Stirling Calder, stands to the south of the school's Scott Library. Thomas Eakins also immortalized Dr. Gross in his painting, "The Gross Clinic," which hangs at the university today. Dr. Gross's native tongue, before he seriously embarked on a medical career, was a German dialect spoken by the Pennsylvania Dutch. Although he graduated from Jefferson, he did not resume his association with the medical college until he joined the faculty at the age of 51.

Dr. Gross is generally acknowledged as the greatest physician Jefferson produced. Although he was the recipient of many tributes, perhaps the most apt was that of W. D. Yandell, who studied under Gross: "A master of surgery, he filled chairs in four medical Colleges.... He recast surgical science as taught in North America, formulated anew its principles, enlarged its domain, added to its art and imparted fresh impetus to its study."

Following Gross, who came to Jefferson in 1856, J. Marion Sims, class of 1835 and a native of South Carolina, was perhaps Jefferson's next graduate of importance. He was one of the great gynecologists of the 19th century, and was responsible for the first successful procedure for the repair of vesicovaginal fistulae. This contribution alone entitles him to an honored place in medical annals. Before this time, women afflicted with this condition were classified as incurable. Sims operated on and treated many slaves before the Civil War, lecturing as he operated. It was he who founded the first college hospital (Woman's Hospital of the State of New York) exclusively for women.

Jefferson was fortunate to attract some of the brilliant medical minds of the past century—and of the present one. Among them was Jonathan Letterman, M.D., who conceived the medical evacuation system used during the Civil War, a technique for removing and treating the wounded that still has application today.

Dr. William Williams Keen, a student of Gross, is best remembered as the first American neurosurgeon—the first to tap the ventricles of the brain and one of the first to remove a brain tumor successfully. It was he who participated in the "secret operation" on President Grover Cleveland in 1893. Because of the state of the economy, the President insisted on absolute secrecy; the country was in a financial crisis, and Cleveland feared a collapse of the stock market if his illness were known. Dr. Keen was also called upon to examine Franklin D. Roosevelt at Campobello, New Brunswick, when the President was stricken with poliomyelitis. This remarkable physician served in the Civil War, volunteered for duty in the Spanish-American War, and at the age of 80 was the oldest member of the Medical Reserve Corps in World War I.

In our own time, two men (among many who for reasons of space cannot be mentioned) have brought lustre to the history of Jefferson – Chevalier Jackson, Sr., and John H. Gibbon, Jr. Dr. Jackson has been justly called "one of the greatest if not the greatest laryngologists of our time." At various times, he held chairs in five of the city's medical colleges, was credited with saving the lives of more than 5,000 children and was responsible for having President Coolidge sign the Federal Caustic Poison Law – which put skull and crossbones on the labels of dangerous bottles in American medicine chests.

Dr. John H. Gibbon, Jr., belonged to the third generation of a family of physicians connected with Jefferson. This self-effacing man worked quietly, with the assistance of his able wife Mary Hopkinson, to perfect the cardio-pulmonary bypass – "the heart-lung machine." In 1931, while keeping an all-night vigil at the bedside of a dying woman, it occurred to him that he could have reduced her massive pulmonary embolism if some of her blood could have been withdrawn into an apparatus where it could absorb oxygen, discharge carbon dioxide and then be returned to her arteries. This revelation resulted more than two decades later in the machine that has enabled doctors to do more than 10,000 operations around the world. Most of the developmental expense was shouldered by Dr. Gibbon himself. (Even the Russians did not try to claim this invention – a Dr. Vishnevski bought ten of the machines and took them back to the U.S.S.R., but royalties were paid to Jefferson.)

ROBERT MILLS HOUSE
228 South Ninth Street

This historic Philadelphia residence, built in the Georgian style, should not be overlooked. Located on the campus of Thomas Jefferson University, it was built in 1809. It is the only documented house designed by Robert Mills (1781-1855), one of the first trained American architects who, after 1812, designed new office buildings – known as "State House Row" – to replace the old wings of Independence Hall. This particular dwelling was part of "Franklin Row," one of 10 residences along the west side of Ninth Street. The brick fanlight-shaped arches over the door and the large windows on the first and second floors are unusual. This curved effect is even carried out in the small dormer, which looks like a half-opened eye on the roof.

Although the house was built before Jefferson Hospital was founded, there is by coincidence a direct link with President Thomas Jefferson. Among his many other accomplishments, our third president was a fine architect. Mills worked under Jefferson at Monticello for two years and then went on to study with Benjamin Henry Latrobe. This surviving example of his domestic architecture in Philadelphia was preserved during the razing of other area buildings for the university's expansion. It is being considered as the residence of the president of Thomas Jefferson University.

CHRIST CHURCH BURIAL GROUND
Fifth and Arch Streets

This ancient burying ground, which has been here since 1719, is especially hallowed because it contains the bones of five Signers of the Declaration of Independence. Two of these concern us because of their medical associations. Benjamin Franklin (1706-1790), the most famous citizen Philadelphia has had, was very much involved in every aspect of the

CHRIST CHURCH BURIAL GROUND

city's life, including medicine. It was he and Dr. Thomas Bond who were responsible in 1751 for founding Pennsylvania Hospital, the first in the country.

Franklin was in advance of even some of the medical men of his time in his advocacy of fresh air, exercise and temperance, and is credited with the invention of bifocal glasses. He also invented a catheter for his brother's use as well as an electrostatic machine that was used to help treat paralysis, deafness and insanity. He took great interest in young Americans studying medicine in Europe and advised and helped William Shippen, Jr., Thomas Parke, George Logan and John Morgan — all 18th century Philadelphia physicians — when they were studying abroad. He was honored by the profession — Benjamin Rush and Caspar Wistar dedicated theses to him — and his kindness to physicians was legendary.

In 1767, when Franklin was in London representing Pennsylvania, he and his son rented rooms in the home of a widow, Mrs. Mary Stevenson, who had a lovely daughter Mary (Polly). The good "doctor," as he was then referred to, was fascinated by this bright child and hoped his son would eventually marry her. This was not to be, but Polly did marry a brilliant doctor, William Hewson, and Franklin advised them on many matters. When Dr. Hewson died in 1774, Franklin urged Polly to emigrate to Philadelphia with her three children, which she finally did in 1786.

The aging Franklin placed the two boys in the University of Pennsylvania, and the Hewsons became a famous and greatly respected Philadelphia medical family. Thomas graduated in 1789, the year before Franklin's death, studied medicine in London and returned to Philadelphia in 1800, thus continuing a medical dynasty and providing a medical link with Benjamin Franklin that continued well into the 19th century.

There are two other graves here of interest. Dr. Benjamin Rush (1746-1813), the site of whose house is now a garden at Third and Walnut Streets and who was the most famous doctor to sign the Declaration of Independence, lies here. He married the daughter of Richard Stockton, another Signer, and was the progenitor of a large and still numerous Philadelphia family. Near him lies Dr. Philip Syng Physick (1768-1837), whose home — the Hill-Physick-Keith House — can be visited at Fourth and Delancey Streets. After an attack of fever, which may have been typhoid, in 1813, Dr. Physick never regained his former vigor. He suffered from renal calculus and cardiac disease from that time until his death. These many years of illness may have given him a peculiar outlook on things. We are told that he "took remarkable measures to avoid the possibility that he might be buried alive and to prevent an autopsy being performed on his body. He left particular instructions that a guard be stationed at his grave to prevent his body being carried away." This is interesting, especially in light of Dr. Physick's own advocacy of autopsy.

Dr. John Kearsley is thought to have been one of the architects of

Christ Church, owner of the burial ground, although this has never been verified by historians.

One block away from this burial ground, on the corner of Fourth and Arch Streets, the medical school of the College of Philadelphia (now the University of Pennsylvania) was founded in 1765, the first medical school in British North America and thus the oldest in the United States.

PENNSYLVANIA COLLEGE OF PODIATRIC MEDICINE
Eighth and Race Streets

The youngest of the colleges for the health sciences (founded in 1960), the Pennsylvania College of Podiatric Medicine – under the direction of James E. Bates, D.P.M. – came into being when Temple University closed its school of podiatry in 1960. The closing inspired members of the faculty to join podiatrists throughout the Delaware Valley in founding the college.

Podiatry in America began in Philadelphia – as did so many other health sciences. Maxwell Whiteman in *Mankind and Medicine* tells us: "Few could boast a recommendation from such an esteemed personage as a president of the United States, but M. Cohen, the city's pioneer chiropodist, claimed to have put a president back on his feet, and published a letter from President John Tyler to prove it."

The first podiatrist's office in the United States was at 11 Bonsall Street, between Ninth and Tenth Streets, south of Lombard. The city directory for 1841 listed Julius Davidson, "chiropodist," at that address, but he did not remain the only podiatrist for long. Soon Isachar Zacharie opened an office, and later both Davidson and Zacharie had offices in the 900 block of Chestnut Street.

The Civil War brought Zacharie to a position of prominence. Soon after the hostilities began, he obtained an audience with Edwin M. Stanton, Lincoln's controversial Secretary of War. Zacharie proposed to Stanton that he organize a corps of podiatrists to accompany the Union armies. The Secretary refused, but it appears Zacharie had a behind-the-scenes role to play on the stage of history. He was called to the White House many times to treat President Lincoln, and letters uncovered years afterward disclosed that Zacharie was sent on confidential missions to the Confederacy.

From such beginnings podiatry grew. (It was then known as chiropody; the name was changed in 1958.) New York licensed podiatrists in 1895, and in that year the first association of podiatrists was formed. This actually led, in 1898, to the founding in New York of the first school, which

PENNSYLVANIA COLLEGE OF PODIATRIC MEDICINE

lasted only nine years. In 1911 and 1912 (in the latter year the first national association, the precursor of today's American Association of Podiatry, was founded), three schools were opened—one in New York and two in Chicago. By 1915, Temple University had started its program. Thus the entire history of podiatry in the United States is only 135 years old.

The present college began in a modest way. In 1963, it occupied a room rented from the Pennsylvania College of Optometry and had only 23 students and one full-time faculty member. Only two years later, the college acquired the former Skin and Cancer Hospital building at Eighth and Pine Streets. Before long, it was overcrowded; highly qualified applicants had to be turned away; and the hours of the clinic were lengthened in order to care for the number of patients who came for treatment from all parts of the Delaware Valley.

Ten years after its founding, in September, 1973, the college moved to its present striking building opposite Metropolitan Hospital and the greenery of Franklin Square. It houses the world's most modern center of podiatric education and foot health care and is one of only five such colleges in the United States that trains specialists in foot care.

HISTORICAL SOCIETY OF PENNSYLVANIA

1300 Locust Street

In a city singularly blessed with great museums and libraries, the Historical Society of Pennsylvania remains unrivalled. It is the scholar's retreat, the researcher's haven. Having undergone extensive expansion and alterations in preparation for the Bicentennial, it is now able to receive additional collections and display the ones it has to greater advantage.

These collections are so vast that a catalogue of even its medical papers and manuscripts would be impossible in a limited space. Among the highlights are the minutes of the Philadelphia Medical Society and Institute for 1817-1853, the record books of the United States Sanitary Commission and Fair, 1861-1873, and papers of physicians: the lecture notes of John Ashurst, the prescription book, 1767-1768, of Thomas Cadwalader, notes by Charles Sellers of Nathaniel Chapman's lectures in 1828, the receipt book for 1787-1796 of John Foulke.

Concerned with drugs and the drug trade are such items as the business papers (1762-1768) of Christopher and Charles Marshall, drug manufacturers; the day book of a drugstore in Norristown, Pennsylvania, for

HISTORICAL SOCIETY OF PENNSYLVANIA

1850-1851; and a remarkable volume, circa 1793, which contains receipts and cures. Also of interest is the casebook of Mrs. Joseph Farber, midwife, covering the years 1814-1831.

There are things to see as well as to read: a pair of apothecary scales that belonged to Dr. Richard Collins, of Collins Mills, New Jersey; a thermometer once the property of Thomas Jefferson and given by him to Dr. Robley Dunglison; and a pair of heavy gold spectacles that belonged to Dr. Caspar Wistar. There is even a bottle of Husband's Calcinated Magnesia, which was manufactured in a factory in Byberry, Pennsylvania, in the late 1840's, as well as apothecary scales and weights belonging to Israel J. Grahame, who had a drugstore at 12th and Filbert Streets in Philadelphia (Grahame was also a professor of pharmacy at the Maryland College of Pharmacy, Baltimore, in the late 1850's).

We can see how the doctors of another age attired themselves, for there are articles of clothing here as well: a vest that belonged to Dr. George Logan in 1798 and a yellow waistcoat that he also wore.

Dr. Elisha Kent Kane, whose body lay in state in Independence Hall, is recalled by a rifle given him in 1856 by George W. Childs, the Philadelphia publisher, and a telescope he used in his expedition to discover the Open Polar Sea.

The Society's collection contains more than 800 portraits and miniatures by early American artists—the finest collection of its kind in America. Two of these interest us. Dr. George Logan (1753-1821), who received his medical degree from Edinburgh in 1779, was painted handsomely by Gilbert Stuart about 1803-1804, and John Morgan (1735-1789), who was in the first graduating class (1757) of what is now the University of Pennsylvania, was painted by Thomas Spence Duché. Dr. Morgan, a founder of the University of Pennsylvania medical school, received his degree from Edinburgh in 1763, was professor of the theory and practice of medicine at the new medical school in 1765, and was later a staff member of Pennsylvania Hospital.

From April 1 through November 30, 1976, the society will be open to the public seven days a week, 9:00 to 9:00. Admission is free.

LIBRARY COMPANY OF PHILADELPHIA
1314 Locust Street

The starkness of the contemporary facade gives no indication of the age of the Library Company (founded 1731) or the extent of its collection—the largest of American printed medical material covering the years 1668-1820 in Philadelphia. Even this statement does not prepare the student, the researcher or the curious for the treasures carefully preserved within.

The great collection of Dr. Benjamin Rush (over 6,000 items) consists of shelves of books, boxes of letters and manuscripts. It was given to the Library Company by his son, Dr. James Rush, who discontinued his practice when the University of Pennsylvania failed to appoint him to his father's chair. Dr. William Logan, of Bristol, England, is represented by his library, the gift of his nephew William Logan. It is a representative library of an early 18th century physician.

The Library Company is rich in 17th century medical books printed in England and on the Continent and contains the only known volumes that belonged to Henry Vaughan, the metaphysical poet who was also a physician. There are batches of papers here of Mathew Carey, the Philadelphia medical publisher, dealing with yellow fever, and also the original manuscript of the Report of the Citizens Committee during the epidemic of 1793. Here, too, is Isaac Norris's copy of Tryon's *Way to Health*. Benjamin Franklin mentioned this work in his *Autobiography*. Shelves of medical books not American and printed after 1700 are side by side with marvelous engravings of the anatomy and musculature (1747). Others showing the skeletal structure of man and animals (1733) by William Cheselden feature jawbones, diseased bones, individual bones. Alexander Monro is represented by such a folio (1783), with plates of the nervous system.

Dr. Rush's copy of the thesis Dr. Philip Syng Physick wrote at Edinburgh is preserved, as is a complete collection of books on malignant fever, a copy of *everything* Dr. John Morgan ever wrote, a tremendous collection of herbals, a collection of works on syphilis published in Venice in 1566, and Gesner's first zoology (1551-1558), with crude but fascinating drawings. In addition to the herbals, there are Hughes's *American Physician* (1672), and some of W.P.C. Barton's watercolors for his *Vegetable Materia Medica* (1817).

Of special interest is the almost complete copy (only three leaves missing) of the photographs of Eadweard Muybridge, showing men, women, and animals in action. In 1887, he published *Animal Locomotion* and in 1893 *Descriptive Zoopraxography*, and the Library Company bought them at the time. This eccentric photographer, often called "the father of the motion picture," photographed nude men and women, in addition to animals, in every kind of activity. His photographs were of value to medical students, physicians and veterinarians at a time when it was unthinkable to photograph the unclothed figure.

II TO THE NORTH

*As we proceed north, we pass through the historic North-
ern Liberties—a section of the present city just outside the
boundaries of William Penn's original plan for Philadelphia. Moving past City Hall, we go as far north as
the Olney section. The great German immigration in the
19th century brought to this area thousands of Germans
(as distinguished from those of the 17th and 18th
centuries who settled in Germantown) along with Irish
and Jews. Most of the institutions discussed here are just
east and west of Broad Street, often referred to as "the
longest street in America."*

HAHNEMANN MEDICAL CENTER
Broad Street to 15th Street, between Race and Vine Streets

The statue of William Penn by Alexander Milne Calder atop
City Hall can be seen from any of the buildings of the Hahnemann
complex — as Hahnemann Medical Center can also be observed from the
statue of the founder of Philadelphia. And if any section of the city can be
identified with the heartbeat of Penn's "Greene Countrie Towne," it is the
area adjoining Centre Square (now City Hall Square), the focus of Penn's
original city.

The multifaceted Hahnemann complex began modestly over a century
and a quarter ago, the result of a meeting in February 1848 at the home of
Dr. Jacob Jeanes. Meeting with him were Drs. Walter Williamson and
Constantine Hering. At this time, no institution in the world taught homeopathy. Earlier there had been the Allentown Academy, chartered in 1836,
which awarded the degree of Doctor of Homeopathia. Dr. Hering had been
associated with the school, which gave instruction in the principles of
Samuel Hahnemann: small doses of drugs, single drugs as opposed to
drastic prescriptions containing numerous drugs, the abolition of blood-
letting, purging, and emesis as cure-alls, and the humane treatment of the
insane. Instruction at the academy was in German. The school continued
for several years and then was disbanded and the buildings were sold to
liquidate the mortgage.

In 1844, the homeopathic physicians formed a national society —
the American Institute of Homeopathy — but there was strong protest
against it, and the American Medical Association at its founding meeting
in 1847 condemned it on principle.

Drs. Jeanes, Williamson and Hering felt, however, that a college of
homeopathy was needed, and the first meeting of the corporators for such
a college was held at the Athenaeum of Philadelphia on Washington
Square. (One of the early trustees was John Sartain, the well-known
Philadelphia engraver.)

Rooms were rented in the rear of 229 (later 635) Arch Street. The
building itself had been used in the past for many purposes: as a schoolroom
and also as a meeting room for the Church of the New Jerusalem (Swedenborgian). In this modest way, the Homoeopathic Medical College of
Pennsylvania in Philadelphia was opened on Monday, October 16, 1848;
the first lecture was given to 15 students, who were to be grounded in the
new medical discipline. In 1849, the college petitioned the Pennsylvania
Legislature for permission to award the degrees of Doctor of Medicine and
Doctor of Homeopathy.

Confidence was such two years later that the college moved to rented

HAHNEMANN MEDICAL CENTER

quarters at 1105 Filbert Street (once occupied by the defunct Philadelphia College of Medicine), its home for the next 35 years.

At a meeting on October 1, 1850, it was decided that any clergyman applying to the dean and paying the matriculation fee should receive a general ticket of admission to the entire course of lectures, but this did not entitle him to become a candidate for a diploma. The following year, the first issue of *The Philadelphia Journal of Homeopathy* appeared, and a building at 24th and Chestnut Streets, near the Schuylkill River, was leased for a homeopathic hospital.

From the time the college purchased the Filbert Street property in 1855, the corporation struggled under a load of debt, and although stock had been issued and other means used to raise money, in 1864 members of the management were discouraged. The faculty was entirely reorganized, new men joined it, and the session of 1864-1865 introduced a new era.

In 1869, when The Female Medical College (1850) changed its name to The Woman's Medical College, the Homeopathic College merged with another small medical college to become Hahnemann Medical College.

Hahnemann was named for Samuel Hahnemann (1755-1843), a native of Meissen, Germany, who had been educated at Leipzig and Erlangen. An early exponent of homeopathy, his belief was that the "body had naturally endowed powers of combatting disease, and that the objective treatment should be to stimulate these natural mechanisms." Homeopathy was never the sole method of treatment taught at the college. It was, instead, a supplement to the orthodox curriculum. As advances in scientific medicine took place, the believers in homeopathy became fewer. However, the last homeopathic course requirement was dropped from the curriculum as late as 1945, and the last homeopathy-elective course as recently as 1959. No degrees in homeopathy have been granted since 1950.

At a meeting on September 23, 1865, it was voted by the faculty to allow ladies to sit in the anteroom to listen to lectures. In 1871, there was further discussion about the admission of women students, but in 1886, when the Women's Medical Club of Philadelphia asked that Hahnemann be opened to women, a courteous letter of refusal was sent to the petitioners. It was not until 1941 that the first women medical students were admitted. Now women students are a familiar sight at Hahnemann.

Almost a century ago, in 1882, a lot on Broad Street between Race and Vine Streets was purchased for $10,000 as the site of the medical school. Three years later the Homeopathic Medical Hospital of Philadelphia (chartered 1874) merged with the Hahnemann Medical College of Philadelphia and the corporate name was changed to Hahnemann Medical College and Hospital. For 94 years the college and hospital have continued to serve faithfully and well the immediate community and the city at large.

In 1890, a 150-bed facility on North 15th Street was dedicated and at the same time a two-year school of nursing was established. In 1898, 50 years after its founding, Hahnemann had a faculty of 16 professors, 14 lecturers and 6 demonstrators, a hospital corps of 38 physicians and surgeons, and a dispensary corps of 70—a far cry from the seven teachers of 1848. The hospital continued to serve at its original location until 1928, when a new 600-bed facility was opened at 230 North Broad Street. In that year, the Medical College moved to the old hospital site at 235 North 15th Street.

During recent years, the institution has continued to make advances. Hahnemann can point with pride to pioneer research in hypertension; computerized electrocardiograms and the development of the pacemaker for heart patients; Dr. Charles P. Bailey's accomplishments in open heart surgery (the Mary Bailey Institute for Heart Research is named for his adopted daughter); and the first identical kidney transplant on twins. The addition of radioisotopes, ultrasound and super-voltage radiation therapy in the Department of Radiology has been of major importance: the department has a six-million electron volt radio-therapy linear accelerator to treat patients needing super-voltage radiation for tumors.

In 1967, a day hospital for the care of mentally ill patients needing intensive treatment but not requiring 24-hour hospitalization was opened as part of the Community Health Program under the Department of Psychiatry. In that year, also, the National Institutes of Health awarded Hahnemann a five-year grant to undertake research to detect cancer in women. The Magee Memorial Hospital affiliated with Hahnemann the following year.

In addition to the Hahnemann Medical College, there are the Graduate School of Medicine and the College of Allied Health Professions. The degrees of Associate in Science, Bachelor of Science, Master of Science, Doctor of Philosophy, Doctor of Psychology and Doctor of Medicine are granted.

Almost 13 decades have passed since the rooms were rented in the small building on Arch Street. Now the Hahnemann complex encompasses a $2.4-million nurses' residence and classroom building, a $34-million college building, a $3-million Bobst clinical research building, and a $2-million Myer Feinstein Polyclinic, among its other facilities. There are some 4,000 living alumni — nearly every county in Pennsylvania is served by Hahnemann Medical College alumni. Three physicians meeting in a room lit with oil lamps in 1848 had a dream — but none conceived how true it would become.

WILLS EYE HOSPITAL
16th and Spring Garden Streets

Wills Eye Hospital was the first hospital in the Western Hemisphere specially devoted to the eye. It was founded in 1832 and was the third hospital of any kind to be established in Philadelphia.

In 1821, two years after graduation from the University of Pennsylvania medical school, Dr. George McClellan announced that a free eye clinic, the first in America, would be located in his office on Swanick Street — from which he later launched the Jefferson Medical College in 1824. By this later date, his eye clinic seems to have ceased operation, perhaps because he was sidetracked by his efforts in getting the new medical school under way. He may also have known of the plan that James Wills, Jr., a Quaker merchant, had to leave his money for a hospital for the care and treatment of the eye. Wills died in 1825, and Wills Eye Hospital owes its existence to his generosity. In that year, the population of Philadelphia was 138,000. Of this number, 69 were physicians and 25 "cuppers and leechers."

The Wills legacy amounted to $108,396.35, but by the time the hospital was built it had increased to $122,548.57. His will directed the establishment of "The Wills Hospital for the Relief of the Indigent Blind and Lame." The site chosen for it was a property extending from Sassafras (now Race) Street to Cherry, from Schuylkill Fourth (19th Street) to Schuylkill Fifth (18th Street), facing Logan Square. (A Philadelphia topographical idiosyncrasy at that time — since abandoned — was to number streets from the Delaware River to Broad Street, and from the Schuylkill River to Broad, beginning in each case with First or Front Street.)

Dr. Squier Littell, attending surgeon from 1834 to 1864, stated:

"Logan Square will furnish a cool, umbrageous promenade, where the eye of the invalid may repose on an extensive field of verdure, relieved at intervals by clustering trees and rendered more grateful and refreshing by its contrast with the busy scene without."

The new hospital, designed by Thomas U. Walter (the architect responsible for the House and Senate wings of the national Capitol) opened on March 3, 1834, with Bishop William White officiating at the dedication. Bishop White had been chaplain of the Continental Congress and later of the Senate, as well as the first Episcopal Bishop of Pennsylvania.

Until the opening of Wills, the care of eye diseases was regarded as but one of many general surgical responsibilities; ophthalmology was not accepted as a separate science. Among the early supporters of the hospital was the Parrish family. Joseph Parrish (1779-1840) had been a pupil of Caspar Wistar. Isaac Parrish (1811-1852), one of the first surgeons in attendance at Wills, was noted for his lectures, which were among the first in the country on ophthalmological topics and set the standard for the physicians to follow. Isaac Hays (1796-1879), also one of the first surgeons at Wills, was the editor of the *Philadelphia Journal of the Medical and Surgical Sciences*. (He and his son, I. Minis Hays, edited it for over a period of 75 years.) He was responsible for a number of instruments for operating on the eye. The knife-needle, the most popular of these, was used for cataract operations. Dr. William E. Horner was the author of "Description of a Small Muscle at the Internal Commissure of the Eyelids," a discovery of

WILLS EYE HOSPITAL

great importance, showing the relationship of this muscle, the tensor tarsi, to the lacrimal apparatus.

In 1837, the hospital could report: "Twenty patients, twelve males and eight females, the house is now full." Soon afterward, the managers were saddened "that no provision had been made in the hospital for people of color," an oversight subsequently corrected. John McAllister, Jr., the son of the recognized founder of optometry in America and also of a family business of opticians, was manager of Wills from 1848 until 1854 and again from 1857 to 1859. In 1828, a Reverend Mr. Goodrich consulted with McAllister on astigmatism. McAllister provided him with a glass ground plane on one side and to a section of a cylinder on the other. These are thought to be the first plano-cylindrical lenses ground in the United States to correct myopic astigmatism.

The provision of Wills' bequest stated the hospital was to be for the lame as well as the blind, and we learn that in 1841 Isaac Parrish performed an operation on a case of clubfoot with the entire staff in attendance. "A Case of Excision of the Thigh Bone" was listed in 1857. By the late 1870's, the last case of lameness was treated by Dr. Henry E. Goodman.

The hospital was fortunate in the caliber of the men on its staff. Among them were Addinell Hewson, a member of the family of physicians that produced William Hewson, Thomas Tickell Hewson and others; William Hunt, who treated Oliver Wendell Holmes, Jr. (later Justice of the United States Supreme Court), during the Civil War; Dr. Richard J. Levis, who devised a wire loop for the removal of the lens from the eye and also a probe to dilate strictures in the lacrimal canal; and Dr. Fitzwilliam Sargent, associated with Wills from 1842 to 1857, who resigned to live in Italy, where his son, John Singer Sargent, the brilliant painter, was born. D. Hayes Agnew, usually associated with Pennsylvania Hospital and the medical school of the University of Pennsylvania (he was also called in to treat President Garfield, felled by an assassin's bullet), was attending surgeon at Wills from 1864 to 1868 and devoted 145 pages of his *Treatise on the Principles and Practice of Surgery* to ophthalmology.

By 1860, the practice of general surgeons devoting some of their time to ophthalmology was passing and ophthalmology as a specialty was developing. Most of the staff at Wills served in the Medical Corps during the Civil War. (Next to Washington, D.C., Philadelphia became the largest hospital center during the war. By December 1864, there were 15 military hospitals in and near Philadelphia, with a total bed capacity of 14,508. Only Washington had more with 24,426.) In 1868, Dr. William McClure invented his iris scissors and William Thomson soon undertook tests for color blindness. S. Weir Mitchell demonstrated that headaches and other nervous reflexes were often due to eye strain and he contributed a chapter on "Diseases of the Eye" to Samuel D. Gross's *System of Surgery.*

The management of the hospital was vested (1870) in the newly created Board of Directors of City Trusts, which has continued to guide its destiny since.

As the 19th century progressed, the increasing space needs of the hospital became more pressing and two ward wings, two surgical suites and a pathology laboratory were added. As early as 1909 all available space on the Logan Square property was in use and the hospital began to think of new and larger, more modern quarters. It was not until 1932, however, that the new hospital at 16th and Spring Garden Streets was opened.

There are no interns at Wills; ophthalmology is a graduate regimen. There are 31 residents and some 20 Fellows working in special areas. Wills Eye Hospital is in truth the graduate school for ophthalmologists.

Now that the hospital has almost reached its own Sesquicentennial, it is seeking once again to expand its facilities to build a new and larger hospital to serve the community. Wills has formed an affiliation with Thomas Jefferson University (the Ophthalmologist-in-Chief is also chairman of the Department of Ophthalmology at Jefferson). Following the Bicentennial a new Wills Eye Hospital will rise on Ninth Street, between Locust and Walnut Streets. James Wills' legacy for the preservation, restoration and care of sight launched the long saga of Wills, of which it has been said: "No other institution in America has been of so great influence in the education of physicians in that branch of medicine."

THE PHILADELPHIA COUNTY MEDICAL SOCIETY
2100 Spring Garden Street

At midpoint in the 19th century, Philadelphia medicine felt the need to organize itself to work for the betterment of the profession and to improve the health of the community. The Philadelphia County Medical Society was not intended to replace the Medical Society of the State of Pennsylvania (1848), but became a constituent part of that organization. Earlier there had been the Philadelphia Medical Society, organized in 1789, which merged with the College of Physicians 50 years later.

The hall of the Philadelphia College of Pharmacy at Seventh and Zane Streets was the setting for the new society's first meeting on January 16, 1849. There were 30 members present; 47 physicians had already subscribed to its constitution and bylaws. Dr. Samuel Jackson, who had been a medical officer in the War of 1812, was its first president.

"Indeed, the founders of The Philadelphia County Medical Society, and those counted among its earliest members, visualized in outline the

THE PHILADELPHIA COUNTY MEDICAL SOCIETY

plan of organization of the medical profession subsequently adopted by the American Medical Association; they showed by this official action the foresight and prophetic wisdom characteristic of master minds." So wrote James M. Anders, M.D., on the occasion of the society's 75th anniversary.

Involvement in the health and welfare of the city and county was the society's watchword from the beginning. Some of the resolutions give evidence of this: one asking that the legislature of Pennsylvania enact a law for the registrations of marriages, births and deaths; another recommending that power be granted by the legislature to each county in the state to provide for the general practice of vaccination; and another urging the laying out of public parks in the more crowded sections of the city, with a view to lessening infantile diseases during the hot months.

The society, desiring to promote the interests not only of the medical profession but also of the general public, urged physicians to familiarize themselves with *The United States Pharmacopoeia* and to adhere to it strictly in their prescriptions. It also urged them to write these legibly. There was concern with the city's water supply, yellow fever in the southern sections of the city (1870), the relation of the milk supply to typhoid fever, and an attempt to reestablish clinical instruction in the wards of Blockley (the Philadelphia General Hospital). They were involved in questions concerning inspection of meat and milk, tuberculosis, and "the reputed perils of the trolley system of transportation." In 1879, the society adjourned a meeting for five minutes so the members could examine the case of Filaria

51

in the eye of a living horse! The first woman member—Dr. Mary Willets—
was elected to membership in 1888, but it was not until 1968 that another—
Dr. Katharine R. Boucot Sturgis—was named president of the society.

The early precepts run through the society's history like a recurring
theme. More than 125 years later, the society still concerns itself with
involvement in community health and community planning, medical
ethics (there has been a committee on this matter for over 25 years), and
help to the physician in the conduct of his practice. The society receives
grievances of the public and attempts to solve them, advises on current
problems—such as health insurance for the layman or the malpractice
issue for the doctor—and during the late 1960's, it opened its doors to the
community in an effort to bring into public discussion any health problems
about which the community was in a quandary.

In 1965, the society moved from its old quarters at 21st and Spruce
Streets to the handsome new building on Spring Garden Street, where it
publishes its monthly magazine, *Philadelphia Medicine.*

THOMAS EAKINS HOUSE
1729 Mount Vernon Street

This house is a relic of time past. It has been rehabilitated, but is in
a declining neighborhood. The house has been repainted and
cleaned and is now administered by the Philadelphia Museum of Art. It
was the home for most of his life of the American artist Thomas Eakins
(1844-1916). The house received a Federal grant for restoration as a community center, and Eakins's fourth floor studio will be refurnished as it was
when he lived and painted here.

Now acknowledged as one of America's artistic giants, Eakins was for
most of his life outside the then-mainstream of American art. If ever genius
fought an uphill battle against odds, Eakins did. Acceptance in Philadelphia
during his lifetime was more difficult than it might have been elsewhere.

Although not born here, Eakins came to live in the house in his 13th
year. It was to be his home for all his creative life—except for short excur-
sions elsewhere, such as four years in Europe and occasional forays to the
then-desolate New Jersey seashore.

At one time, he studied anatomy at Jefferson Medical College, and
historians are agreed that the thought of pursuing a medical career was in
his mind. The years at Jefferson under Dr. Pancoast bore fruit in his lifelong
obsession with the medical profession and anatomy. As John Canaday, the
art critic and historian, wrote: "Eakins's passion was anatomy. For him the
human body was the most beautiful thing in the world—not as an object
of desire, or as a set of proportions, but as a construction of bone and

muscle." Eakins spent two years (1864-1865) at Jefferson "to increase his knowledge of how beautiful objects are put together."

This passion culminated in his "Portrait of Professor Gross," now known as "The Gross Clinic," which is undoubtedly one of the great medical paintings of all time, perhaps on a par with Rembrandt's "The Anatomy Lesson," but of course great in an entirely different way.

Dr. Samuel D. Gross (then 70 years of age), the pivotal figure in the painting, was chief of surgery at Jefferson Medical College, and posed in Eakins's skylighted studio in the house on Mount Vernon Street. The finished portrait—of an operation to remove a piece of bone diseased by osteomyelitis—caused a sensation. Critics and laymen disliked it intensely when it was exhibited at Hasseltine's Gallery, 1125 Chestnut Street. Philadelphia took offense, and sensibilities were outraged. The man operated on was a charity patient. We can tell this by the woman (obviously his mother) who was present. At that time, the law required that a relative of the charity patient be present (when available) for the operation. Most doctors, wishing to avoid malpractice suits, saw that this was done.

"The Gross Clinic" (1875) was exhibited at the Centennial Exhibition of 1876, not in the art gallery with the other well-known artists (some of Eakins's other paintings were), but in the First Aid Hospital on the exposition grounds in Fairmount Park. It was acquired by Jefferson Medical College in 1878. The purchase price was $200. Today it is worth millions.

"The Agnew Clinic," the other great surgical painting by Eakins, hangs in the medical school of the University of Pennsylvania (it was painted in Eakins's studio at 1330 Chestnut Street, a site now marked by a bronze plaque), commissioned by members of D. Hayes Agnew's class in the medical school. The students, in a display of affection and appreciation to their preceptor, presented it to him at the Academy of Music on May 1, 1889. (Drs. J. William White and Joseph Leidy II are shown in the background.)

Eakins, always fascinated by the world of medicine, continued to paint portraits of doctors. Those of Drs. William Smith Forbes and Benjamin Howard Rand are at Thomas Jefferson University; of Dr. J. Mendez Da Costa at Pennsylvania Hospital; of Dr. Charles Lester Leonard at the University of Pennsylvania; and of Dr. William Thomson at The College of Physicians. Both the Pennsylvania Academy of the Fine Arts and the Philadelphia Museum of Art have extensive Eakins collections of a nonmedical nature. (The museum also has a superb collection—*Ars Medica*—of prints, engravings, etchings, lithographs, mezzotints and woodcuts relating to medicine, presented to it by SmithKline Corporation. Such masters as Blake, Daumier, Dürer, Eakins, Ensor, Gillray, Hogarth, Holbein, Klee, Toulouse-Lautrec, Rembrandt and Watteau are represented.)

Thomas Eakins died in the second-floor middle bedroom at 1729 Mount Vernon Street on June 25, 1916, after having lived there 59 years.

TEMPLE UNIVERSITY HEALTH SCIENCES CENTER
3400 North Broad Street

This vast complex (16 acres), which extends from Allegheny Avenue north to Tioga Street and on both sides of Broad Street to Park Avenue on the east, is the home of Temple University Medical School, Temple University Hospital, Temple University Pharmacy School, Temple University School of Dentistry and the College of Allied Health Professions—one of the four major campuses of Temple University in Philadelphia and the immediate suburbs.

Although many remarkable men and women are responsible for Temple's greatness as a medical school, the credit for its establishment must go to Dr. Russell H. Conwell (1843-1925), the Baptist minister who founded Temple College in 1888 and then aided its growth by singlehandedly stumping the country to bring attention to his "child."

It all began in June 1891, when a small hospital known as The North Philadelphia Hospital, serving this area of the city, was forced to close. Dr. Conwell answered an appeal to undertake its reorganization. A site at the heart of the present campus—on the corner of Broad and Ontario Streets—and a dwelling at 3403 North Broad Street were purchased. The members of the congregation of Dr. Conwell's Grace Baptist Church raised one thousand dollars for the down payment, and in January 1892, a 20-bed hospital—the Samaritan—was dedicated by him. The board of managers ruled the hospital would be for "charity cases that need medical or surgical treatment and still further for acute cases only." Chronic and contagious diseases were to be treated at the dispensary, but not admitted to the hospital.

While the first year was a busy one, even a hectic one (202 patients admitted; 1,028 dispensary cases), the admissions report for March of that year gives an unintentionally humorous picture of the first weeks of operation:"10 patients were discharged; 8 of them cured, 1 relieved and 1 eloped." The word "eloped" had a different connotation medically; it meant the patient discharged himself.

The following year, the Samaritan Hospital School for Nurses was established "to train young women of good moral standing and common school education to nurse the sick, and thus educate them to a position of honor and great usefulness in the community." By 1898, a second building was added to the hospital, the maternity department known as the Greatheart Hospital (named for one of the characters in John Bunyan's *Pilgrim's Progress*).

During the spring of 1901, the Board of Trustees of Temple College opened an evening medical school, the first such school in the nation. Five

54

years' evening instruction were given and the curriculum so arranged that the same number of hours were devoted to it as in a day school. The medical school was also the first coeducational one in Pennsylvania. Although no women were among the 31 students enrolled the first year, in 1907 the school awarded medical degrees to its first women graduates, Drs. Sara Allen and Mary E. Shephard.

Among early giants was Dr. W. Wayne Babcock, who gained international fame as a pioneer in the technique of spinal anesthesia and for his invention of surgical instruments. "The Babcock Surgical Clinic" by Furman J. Finck, a composite portrait in the genre of Eakins's "The Gross Clinic" and "The Agnew Clinic," was commissioned on Dr. Babcock's retirement. Surgeons associated with him at Temple posed with him for this dramatic canvas, which hangs in the university today.

By 1907, with appropriations from the state legislature and funds raised by the local community, a new hospital was erected. One wall, which still forms part of the hospital building, consists of bricks inscribed with the names of donors who contributed one dollar each. That year, too, Temple College was accredited as a university and the school of medicine became a college within the university. Also, the Garretson Hospital allied itself with Temple and afforded unusual facilities and material for teaching "traumatic surgery," which was probably not excelled by any other medical school in the United States.

Temple has always had close affiliations with hospitals in the area. In 1928, the Jewish Hospital (now Albert Einstein Medical Center—Northern

TEMPLE UNIVERSITY HEALTH SCIENCES CENTER

Division) opened its doors to the medical students of Temple University, and many of the faculty at the medical school today are on the staff of the Einstein Center. Its closest association, however, is with Saint Christopher's Hospital, an actual department of the medical school. In 1929, the name of the hospital was changed to the Temple University Hospital to indicate the close relationship between the university and the hospital. In 1930, the Chevalier Jackson Clinic for the treatment of diseases of the air and food passages was opened. The distinguished physician after whom it was named was a staff member of five of the Philadelphia medical schools.

Temple University Hospital (530-bed) has had its own successes through the years. It was here that the first successful pneumonectomy (removal of a lung) in Philadelphia was performed by Dr. W. Emory Burnett in 1938. Drs. O. Spurgeon English and Edward Weiss developed the first clinic for psychosomatic medicine in 1939, and in the following year Dr. Gerald H. J. Pearson founded a pioneer psychiatry clinic. Dr. John A. Kolmer in medicine, Dr. W. Edward Chamberlain in radiology, and Dr. John Royal Moore in orthopedics achieved wide acclaim for original work in their respective fields.

Deep brain surgery demands extraordinary precision and exactness. The first device employed to pinpoint trouble areas, the stereoencephalotome, was developed at Temple by Dr. Ernest A. Spiegel, professor of neurology, and one of his former students, Dr. Henry T. Wycis, a neurosurgeon. Drs. Spiegel and Wycis performed the first operation with the device in 1947, attaching the stereoencephalotome to the patient's skull. This then guided surgical instruments in psychosurgery. An early model of this device is on display at the Smithsonian Institution in Washington, D.C.

During the early years of the Depression, a four-year program leading to a Bachelor of Science in Pharmacy was instituted at Temple University. Temple's course had originally been offered in 1901 as two years of day instruction and three of evening study, but by 1918 the night school was disbanded, and students were matriculated for a three-year course beginning in 1925. Temple's pharmacy school is one of the most progressive in the nation. The School of Dentistry, founded as the Philadelphia Dental College in 1863, became part of Temple in 1907. It is the second oldest dental school in the United States, and the fourth largest.

In 1961 the hospital, the schools and supporting activities were united into the Temple University Health Sciences Center. The Skin and Cancer Hospital opened in 1965 had its beginning in 1928 as a dispensary or out-patient clinic at 806 Pine Street through the initiative of Dr. Albert Strickler. In 1957 it became the dermatology department of the medical school, and in 1973 dissolved its board of trustees and officially came into the Temple corporation. The Health Sciences Center contains the Fels Research Institute for cancer study, and the hospital has an affiliation with the Eastern Pennsylvania Psychiatric Institute. In 1966, the College of Allied Health

Professions was established—offering baccalaureate courses in medical technology, nursing, occupational therapy, physical therapy and the department of health records administration—giving the center even greater dimension.

Temple is ever in the vanguard. This was best illustrated when David Hartman, the first blind student admitted to medical school in this century, entered Temple to study psychiatry. Refused admittance by nine other medical schools, he persisted, and was admitted to Temple—a university imbued with the spirit of adventure first displayed by its founder.

ALBERT EINSTEIN MEDICAL CENTER - NORTHERN DIVISION
Old York and Tabor Roads

Although Jews had settled in Philadelphia as early as the first decade of the 18th century and had established the Mikveh Israel Burial Ground in 1740, there was no Jewish hospital opened in Philadelphia until 1866. There had been, after the Revolution, a Jewish society for visiting the sick and burying the dead. Both Pennsylvania Hospital and the Blockley Almshouse (later the Philadelphia General Hospital) cared for the Jewish sick, and physicians from the Hebrew Relief Society called on indigent patients.

The first action toward the establishment of a Jewish hospital was taken in late 1863, when a number of Jews rented a small house on Powelton Avenue near 34th Street to which the destitute from the almshouse and the public taverns could be admitted. In August 1864, at a meeting of the District Grand Lodges of B'nai B'rith from Pennsylvania, Maryland and the District of Columbia, the need for a Jewish hospital was put forth. Six months later, the largest public meeting of Jews of Philadelphia was held; hundreds of men and women signed the subscription lists. The first contribution—$100—was received from the 84-year-old legendary Rebecca Gratz, who had served as the model for Rebecca in Sir Walter Scott's *Ivanhoe*. Contributions came from hundreds of working people who could only afford a dollar or two.

This intense community activity resulted in the purchase of "Woodside," a large dwelling of almost 25 rooms on three acres at Fisher's Avenue and Haverford Road in Hestonville (in West Philadelphia), almost directly behind Beth El Emeth Cemetery. The Jewish Hospital Association was formed in September 1865. Drs. Jacob Da Silva Solis-Cohen, Manly Emanuel and Benjamin B. Wilson offered their services as consultants without charge, and a year later, on August 6, 1866, the 22-bed Jewish Hospital

ALBERT EINSTEIN MEDICAL CENTER

opened its doors. Contributions of food and equipment came from men and women in all walks of life, among them Morris Rosenbach (his sons Philip and A.S.W. founded the Rosenbach Foundation and museum, now on Delancey Place), who contributed the bed linens. Dr. Adolph Feldstein was the first resident and one of the hospital's first pediatricians. In the first six months of operation, 28 patients were admitted, and the hospital's long record of service began.

One aspect peculiar to Jewish Hospital, and not to others, was the great number of peddlers using its facilities. These men ventured into the rural areas carrying their wares on their backs, and returned each spring to Philadelphia to restock their packs and to spend the Passover in the city. Occupational diseases peculiar to life on the road made them the greatest users of the facilities. Women domestic workers were next. However, from the beginning the hospital was open to all. A few months after it began operation, three non-Jews were admitted. In 1869, there was a time when the number of non-Jewish admissions was greater than those of Jews. The hospital was "free to the suffering poor of all religions." This attitude so impressed Mary D. Brown, a Quaker, that she sent Dillwyn Parrish (son of Dr. Joseph Parrish) to inspect the hospital. Her first contribution was $500, and she made substantial additional ones as the years went by.

In 1869, the United Hebrew Charities was formed and the Jewish Hospital shared in its program. A committee was appointed that same year to determine whether a new building should be erected on the property or

58

a site found elsewhere. The hospital was growing at such a rate that something had to be done. The committee strongly recommended purchasing a property of 14-1/2 acres on Old York Road, north of Branchtown: a mansion, farmer's house, barn and springhouse were on the property. By January 1872, pledges of $30,000 were in hand and work began on the new buildings. The dedication drew the largest gathering of Jews—some 2,500—ever assembled in Pennsylvania for a purpose other than an exclusively religious one. At this time, the Jewish population of Philadelphia was 12,000; 30 years later, it was estimated at 50,000.

The first horse-drawn ambulance was purchased in 1884, and a Home for the Aged opened in 1889. In the 1890's, the staff almost doubled (12 doctors in 1890, 21 in 1900); a nurses' training school was opened in 1892, a gynecological clinic in 1896 and the nose and throat clinic in 1899. Jewish Hospital was a pioneer in outdoor treatment of tuberculosis, and in 1902 a tent of four beds was erected on the lawn for patients with the disease.

There were innovations peculiar to the hospital's location. Because of the frequency of railroad accidents, the Reading Railroad Company established wire communication between the Tabor tower and the hospital. An alarm bell alerted the hospital of a wreck or disaster. The horse-drawn ambulance would then race to the scene of the accident. After one such accident in 1899, Dr. Moses Behrend performed his first surgical operation on the stump of a railroad worker's severed leg. This was the beginning of Dr. Behrend's long and distinguished career at the hospital; he was visiting physician from 1906 until 1913 when he joined the surgical staff and remained a member of it until his retirement in 1948.

The hospital's growth after the beginning of the present century was phenomenal. In 1901, the Federation of Jewish Charities was organized (a successor to the United Hebrew Charities) and the hospital became affiliated with it. Buildings for patients with contagious diseases, a children's ward, a new operating room, and the Guggenheim Building for private patients all extended the hospital's facilities.

About this time, Dr. Solomon Solis-Cohen interested Jules E. Mastbaum (who later gave the city the Rodin Museum) in subsidizing a research project to determine the cause and aid in the prevention of poliomyelitis. Perhaps no one served the hospital as did William B. Hackenburg, who died in 1918. He was director from 1865 to 1869 and treasurer until 1878, when he assumed the presidency, a position he held until his death—a record probably unequalled in Philadelphia.

In the late 1940's, Jewish community leaders proposed the idea of a medical center "devoted to medical teaching, medical research, and community health activity" as well as having an affiliation with a medical school. It was suggested the name for such a center be nonsectarian, even though this hospital had always been so in actual practice. In 1952, it was given its present name (with the approval of the great scientist himself), and Dr.

Pascal F. Lucchesi was named executive vice-president and medical director.

Expansion became even more rapid from that date. A new clinic replaced the dispensary and a medical-surgical building, a modern rehabilitation center, research laboratories and attractive maternity facilities sprang up on the extensive property. Outpatient buildings, psychiatric facilities for children and adults, a department of dentistry, and an affiliation with the Moss Rehabilitation Hospital (on the grounds of the Northern Division) has further extended the center's scope, as has its affiliation with Temple University. The Department of Transplant Immunology and Organ Preservation, established in 1963, has developed to such a degree that there are now six centers in the Greater Philadelphia area. (Their surgeons have formed a Greater Delaware Valley Transplant Society to encourage cooperation in the procurement of cadaver kidneys and to facilitate sharing personnel and facilities.)

The peristyle of six granite columns that once graced the old U.S. Mint at 13th and Chestnut Streets now marks the main entrance to the Northern Division grounds. A link with Philadelphia's past, the entrance adds an historic touch to the modern medical facilities that have done so much to provide sound health care in Philadelphia for the past 110 years.

PENNSYLVANIA COLLEGE OF OPTOMETRY
1200 West Godfrey Avenue

This young and progressive college has, in less than 60 years, grown to be one of the foremost of its kind in America — a leader in Pennsylvania and among similar institutions in other states as well. Founded in 1919 by Dr. Albert Fitch, who served it faithfully until 1960, the college was started specifically as a health professional school — making it, in reality, the first optometric college of its kind in the United States. Some of the university colleges of optometry have evolved from the university physics departments. The college has the distinction of being the first founded specifically as a health professional school.

Optometry, America's third largest independent health care profession, began in Philadelphia with John McAllister (1753-1830), an emigrant to the Colonies from Scotland just before the Revolution. McAllister was a skilled cabinetmaker who made ammunition boxes for the Continental army. By 1781, he had begun producing whips and canes at his shop at Second and Market Streets. When he later expanded his business and acquired the stock of a hardware merchant, he became the owner of a bushel basket of steel-rimmed ready-made spectacles. In this accidental way, Philadelphia became the birthplace of American optometry.

Among McAllister's early clients was George Washington. His son, John, Jr. (1786-1877), carried on the business, not only by supplying spectacles, but also by recommending eye care to Thomas Jefferson, Joseph Bonaparte, Henry Clay and Andrew Jackson. He was the first American to correct the condition known as astigmatism by making cylindrical lenses. This technique, although improved over the years, is still used by optometrists to correct astigmatism. It is only fitting, therefore, that optometry in the 20th century should make such strides in Philadelphia—McAllister's adopted city.

The College of Optometry, a forerunner in many areas—like so many other Philadelphia medical institutions—has its own share of "firsts." It was the first school of optometry to award the Doctor of Optometry (O.D.) degree in 1923; the first to develop a four-year professional curriculum, requiring a minimum of two years of undergraduate education and setting stringent standards for science prerequisites for applicants (with the first baccalaureate degree awarded in 1958); and the first optometric institution to initiate comprehensive continuing education programs for practicing optometrists. It also led the way in introducing into the optometric curriculum new areas of study, such as contact lens education, while emphasizing areas in systematic pathology, such as hypertension and diabetes as they relate to vision care, along with the study of pharmacology, both as to the systematic effects of drugs on the visual system and the use of drugs for the examination of the eye.

PENNSYLVANIA COLLEGE OF OPTOMETRY

Optometry has been thought of as the examining of the eyes and the prescribing of the proper corrective glasses—nothing more. But the profession has come of age, and the college helped lead the way. The college's education program is a broad-based one devoted to health care, patient care and research. Great stress is placed upon the biological sciences at the college, where the most modern laboratories and classroom facilities are available on the 13-acre campus in the Oak Lane section of the city.

There is evidence of the Computer Age at the Pennsylvania College of Optometry. One example is the electrodiagnostic vision examination (partially sponsored by a grant from Lions' International Clubs), which provides refraction and other diagnostic tests for the handicapped patient. Another technique used by college clinicians feeds photographs of the cornea into a computer and the printout tells the doctor what type of contact lens the patient requires.

Great emphasis is placed on infant care at the college. A new clinic that studies the infant's vision has recently been opened, and a pediatric optometry service provides similar services for the older child.

Like many other medical institutions looking to the future, the college has a splendid program for sending pregraduates out to doctors' offices in their fourth year—a variant on the old preceptorship of the 18th and 19th centuries. The program has recently received significant Federal funding for its development.

To keep graduate doctors up-to-date on the changes in their profession, the college has a Division of Continuing and Post-Graduate Education. The purpose of this program is to keep graduate doctors informed about changes in the profession and is based on the concept that optometric education begins during undergraduate professional studies and continues throughout the practitioner's career.

The only school of optometry in Pennsylvania and the major optometric resource for the Middle Atlantic States, the college has more than 3,000 alumni. Dr. Norman E. Wallis, its president since 1972 and only the third in its history, is the youngest college president in optometry and is currently president of the Association of Schools and Colleges of Optometry.

Probably no activity at the college is more indicative of the school's concern for eye care than its volunteer organization of students known as the Student Optometric Service to Haiti. Founded in 1968 by Dr. Algernon Phillips, then a fourth-year student at the college, it has since provided free vision care to thousands of citizens in and around Cap Haitien, Haiti. The program is wholly under the direction of the students and a faculty advisor and is funded by private contributions. Today, there are only two physicians trained to provide any type of vision care for the 60,000 people of Cap Haitien. This concern with the eye problems of the illiterate and poor of this Caribbean republic is characteristic of the Pennsylvania College of Optometry's educational philosophy as it prepares to enter its seventh decade.

III To the South

South Philadelphia — ethnically and geographically —
is a composite of many generations of the foreign born.
In the 17th century, the Swedes and Dutch vied for the
rights to the land in the ancient district later called
Southwark — named for that section of London south of
the Thames that was intimately known to Shakespeare.
In the 18th century, the English came; in the 19th, there
were the great immigrations from Eastern, Central and
Southern Europe: Jews from the ghettoes of Poland,
Rumania, the Baltic area and Russia, and Italians and
Slavs. After the Civil War, the blacks struggled North
from an impoverished South and sought refuge here.

UNITED STATES NAVAL HOME
Grays Ferry Avenue and 24th Street

Few who pass the dramatically impressive Greek Revival edifice
by William Strickland (1788-1854), one of America's foremost
architects, are aware that what is now called the Naval Home began as a
hospital. In the beginning, it was called the Naval Asylum and was located
in the town of Passyunk. In those days—it was established by an Act of
Congress in 1811—the word "asylum" had a different connotation. ("Home"
was substituted for "Asylum" in 1889.) The building was to be a "permanent 'Asylum' for decrepit and disabled naval officers, seamen, and marines."

Actually, the first hospital on the grounds was Pemberton House, the
mansion that once belonged to James Pemberton, a Quaker who by order of
the Committee of Safety was deported to Virginia during the Revolution for
having signed certain papers considered to be against the best interests of
the rebelling colonists. From 1826 until 1833, Pemberton House served as
the fourth Naval Hospital in Philadelphia. (From 1811 to 1826, when the
asylum was opened, a dispensary or sick quarters was used as a Naval
Hospital at the Philadelphia Navy Yard, then located at Delaware and
Snyder Avenues.)

Funds for the hospital were raised in an unusual manner. An Act of
Congress in 1799 provided for the assessment of 20 cents a month from the
pay of all seamen as a "Navy Pension Fund" for the relief of the sick and
disabled. A year before, such an act had been passed in regard to the merchant marine. The money collected was to be paid to the Commissioners of
the Navy Pension Fund and the "officers, seamen, and marines of the Navy
were to receive the same relief as sick and disabled seamen of the merchant
service." The Privateer Pension Fund—which sounds incongruous to our
ears today—accrued from a percentage levied against privateer prizes and
was also placed in the Navy Pension Fund. In 1811, legislation authorized
the Navy to establish a separate Medical Department and the Pension Fund
was converted to a Hospital Fund, used in part to buy and build naval
hospitals.

By 1833, Biddle Hall, with its eight Ionic columns and wide verandas
on each of the wings, was occupied, its south wing housing the Naval
Hospital from that year until 1868. Although the Navy has always had a
reputation for cleanliness and order, a report in 1834 said that the windows
of the asylum were swollen by dampness, that want of fresh air was so great
that parts of the asylum were untenable, the water closets were impure,
and that "a thorough cleansing is absolutely essential to the inmates." What
would astound Philadelphians today is the recommendation to use drinking water from the Schuylkill River nearby rather than from wells on the

UNITED STATES NAVAL HOME

property. Lieutenant James B. Cooper, the superintendent, left it on record that "I really consider Sir, that the introduction of Schuylkill water is one of the most essential conveniences connected with the Establishment."

During the last years of the Civil War, the quartering of hospital patients, beneficiaries and midshipmen in a single building did not prove satisfactory and caused a great many differences. The war itself overtaxed the hospital facilities to such an extent that during the years 1865-1867 a new hospital building was erected just behind Biddle Hall (named for the first Governor of the Naval Home, Captain—later Commodore—James Biddle of Philadelphia, who held the post from 1838 to 1842). Designed by John McArthur, who was responsible for Philadelphia's City Hall, and opened in 1868, it was named Laning Hall. Wounded from the Civil War were cared for here, and it remained the Naval Hospital until 1921. At that time the Public Health Service took over the building, using it until 1932. In 1943, during World War II, it was again used as a hospital, this time for convalescent patients. Ten years after Laning Hall opened, one chronicler reported: "There are in the Institution at this time One Hundred and Forty-One Beneficiaries, and there has been admitted, in all, since its first establishment, Seven Hundred and Eighty-Seven. The increase is very slow, the old men dying, either from accident, the effects of dissipation, or the diseases incident to old age, very nearly as fast as the new ones come in."

In addition to the medical facility once provided here, the grounds provide a point of interest to veterinarians as well. Dexter Park, just behind the Surgeon's House, contains a small gravestone, which records the vital statistics of the last Navy mule:

Dexter
Foaled—1934
U.S. Army Artillery
World War II
Servant & Friend
U.S. Naval Home
For 23 Years
Died—1968

Dexter—long remembered and much honored by his mates—lies some 16 feet below ground, beneath the stone which gives the important biographical data on his life. A sign designates the area as Dexter Park and a flag flutters above him.

Although our interest is medical, it might be pointed out that the Surgeon's House and the Governor's House, which flank Biddle Hall, were erected in 1844 by William Strickland as were the lodges at the gates. The cannon on the abutments were used in the Battle of the Brandywine (1777) and several illustrious Naval names have been associated with the home. Commodore James Barron (1769-1851), court-martialed as commander of the frigate *Chesapeake,* in the incident of 1807, is unfortunately best remembered for killing Stephen Decatur in a duel at Bladensburg, Maryland, in 1820. He was in command of the Philadelphia Station, and was also in charge of the asylum—that being part of the station. In the records of the old hospital appear the names of Lieutenant (later Admiral) David G. Farragut (1801-1870), hero of New Orleans and Mobile Bay in the Civil War, and Isaac Hull, commander of the U.S.S. *Constitution* ("Old Ironsides"). Both were patients at one time.

Twenty acres now remain in this enclave, which contains a half-dozen historic buildings considered by architectural historians to be unique. The Naval Home will move to Gulfport, Mississippi, in 1976 and preservationists are endeavoring to save the buildings and grounds of this historic hospital-home so that they may continue to be used, even if in another capacity.

SAINT AGNES HOSPITAL
1900 South Broad Street

Perhaps no hospital has so touched the lives of Philadelphians as has Saint Agnes Hospital. Its Burn Center—where victims of small fires or large holocausts are rushed—has made Saint Agnes a household word in the city. Administered by the Sisters of Saint Francis of Philadelphia, it exemplifies the city's tradition of Catholic hospitalization.

The history of Catholic nursing stretches back into the 18th century. Sometime after the founding of Saint Joseph's Church in Philadelphia (1733), Sisters came to the city and nursed the sick in the orphanages, almshouses and homes for the poor and the aged. One of the identifiable beginnings was during the cholera epidemic of 1832, when Jesse Burden, a director of the city almshouse, appealed to Bishop Francis Patrick Kendrick to obtain the services of additional nuns to nurse the sick. The Bishop wrote to Mother Elizabeth Seton (now Saint Elizabeth Ann Seton) at Emmitsburg, Maryland, and within hours of receiving his letter she dispatched 13 nuns to nurse the afflicted. They remained there in charge of the almshouse until May 1833, and were offered silver plate (which they refused) by the city fathers in gratitude for their help.

In Philadelphia, the Sisters of Saint Francis trace their beginnings to 1855, when Mrs. Anna Bachmann, a widow, her sister Barbara Boll, and Anna Dorn expressed their wish to be taken into the order. The Reverend John B. Hespelein, rector of Saint Peter's Church, communicated with Bishop John Neumann, who was then in Rome. These three women—all immigrants from Bavaria—became the nucleus of the Franciscan community in Philadelphia. Mrs. Bachmann became Sister Mary Francis, Miss Boll, Sister Mary Margaret, and Miss Dorn, Sister Mary Bernardine. Mother Mary Francis was the first superior of the community, which then numbered only six nuns.

In 1860, Bishop Neumann's successor, Bishop James F. Wood, separated the Sisters in the Central New York missions (Sister Bernardine Dorn among them) from the motherhouse in Philadelphia. Soon afterward (1863), Mother Mary Francis died, and it was left to Mother Bernardine Dorn to carry on the work of the order. Schools, orphanages and hospitals—among them Saint Agnes Hospital at Broad and Mifflin Streets—were founded by this group of dedicated women.

There had been two other Catholic hospitals before Saint Agnes. Saint Joseph's, founded by the Sisters of Charity, was opened in 1849 and Saint Mary, founded by the Sisters of Saint Francis in 1860. In our time, the Sisters of Saint Francis operated Saint Joseph's Hospital during the period 1947 to 1954, although it belonged to the diocese of Philadelphia.

Mother Agnes Bucher, who had taken over the mortgage of Saint Joseph's Hospital in Lancaster, Pennsylvania, was urged by Dr. Andrew Nebinger, who represented the physicians of South Philadelphia, to found a hospital in that section of the city. There was a great need for a hospital, and the task would be formidable. Mother Agnes met the challenge with only $200 in the bank. She sought the sanction of Bishop Wood, who opposed the move, saying the proposed site was too far from the center of population—much of South Philadelphia was country then—and the undertaking seemed hazardous and without sufficient funds to begin with.

Mother Agnes was not to be deterred. After prayer and reflection she again appealed to the Bishop. She chose the day wisely—the Feast of Saint Agnes, her patron. The Bishop acquiesced, and Mother Agnes and the Sisters began a house-to-house canvass of the city. Among those they approached were Francis Drexel and his three daughters, one of whom was later to take vows herself and as Mother Katherine Drexel become a great teacher among blacks and Indians. The Drexels responded generously.

The cornerstone of Saint Agnes was laid in 1882, but the building itself was not opened until 1888. Saint Agnes Hospital is unique in that it has always been at one location, a distinction it shares with such hospitals as Pennsylvania, Friends, and the Hospital of the University of Pennsylvania.

The hospital was a reality at last, but other more pressing realities lay ahead. The Sisters lived frugally but it took more than frugality—often great ingenuity—to survive. There was the time that $100 was set aside to pay for coal, but when Sister Eulalia went to the safe for it, the money had disappeared. Embarrassed at not being able to pay for the coal, the Sisters prayed to Saint Anthony for the money's safe return. At the end of their vigil the money was received in the mail—to great rejoicing. Food was as much a problem as coal. Once when there was no bread for the hospital, several Sisters went into the streets asking for funds. With a dollar given to them by one man they bought bread from a local baker and he, also moved by their plight,more than filled their baskets.

The Drexel sisters, always generous to any charitable appeal, gave the Sisters $30,000 to purchase lots adjoining the hospital property when they were about to be auctioned. The Sisters knew that if houses were built on the lots, the patients might suffer from the noise.

The Sisters of Saint Francis have always felt that the only boundary to the geographical sphere of the hospital is *need* and wherever the need occurred, they responded. Their role in the life of South Philadelphia since the founding of their first hospital in 1860 is evidenced by the affection in which they are held by the community.

Saint Agnes has sought constantly for new ways in which to serve. A neighborhood Medi-Call program was instituted in 1970. It is based on the premise that community health can only be improved by the examination of all individuals and that early detection of illnesses, particularly in their asymptomatic phases, will prevent or at least postpone contingencies and crises. Free diagnostic services include visual acuity, blood pressure, ocular tension measurement by an ophthalmologist, and health teaching.

After being in several stationary locations, the Medi-Call program acquired a mobile health van in 1971 with funds contributed by John Cardinal Krol, Archbishop of Philadelphia. The van is a self-contained unit intended to attract individuals who are unaware that they need medical care, are unable to go to a hospital, or are fearful of doing so.

The van's staff endeavors to break down such prejudices and persuade people to avail themselves of the services Saint Agnes offers the community. When illness is uncovered, the individual is referred to his physician or hospital for definitive evaluation and treatment. The hospital's outpatient department—of which Medi-Call is a part—has been designated as the Cardinal Krol Community Health Center.

The Burn Center, honoring the Fire Fighters of the Greater Delaware Valley, was dedicated in 1974. Its importance was never more vividly brought home to Philadelphians than in August 1975, when a huge oil fire raged for days in South Philadelphia at the Gulf Oil refineries. Eight members of the city's fire department died as a result of the fire. Two of these men were patients at the Burn Center. The Burn Centers of Saint Agnes Hospital and Crozer-Chester Medical Center (in Chester County) are affiliates of the Burn Foundation of the Greater Delaware Valley, a consortium providing facilities for the care and treatment of the severely burned. Both hospitals are affiliated with the Shock-Trauma Network of Hahnemann Medical Center. (Saint Agnes and Hahnemann are also affiliated in the departments of surgery and medicine.)

Almost a century has passed since the little band of Sisters had to beg for money on the streets of Philadelphia for coal and bread for their hospital. Their inspiration then and now has been the words of Mother Mary Agnes Bucher: "...to be poor and sick is the abundantly sufficient credential of an applicant at our doors."

ALBERT EINSTEIN MEDICAL CENTER-DAROFF DIVISION (SOUTHERN)
Fifth and Reed Streets

From that part of South Philadelphia where the Daroff Division stands, City Hall can be seen in the distance on a clear day, with the Benjamin Franklin Bridge beyond. Street after street of brick row houses, typical of this section—punctuated only by the towers of a housing complex —define this part of the city as a "neighborhood," a small town within the country's fourth largest city.

In the decades immediately after the Civil War, when immigration from Central and Eastern Europe—principally Germany, Russia, Poland, Rumania and those parts of the Austro-Hungarian Empire that today comprise Czechoslovakia and Hungary—was at its greatest, many of the Jews who found their way to Philadelphia settled in South Philadelphia. The first enclave was between Second and Seventh and Lombard and Christian Streets. Later the borders were extended further south.

This was the age of the denominational hospital movement, which gained considerable momentum in the last half of the 19th century. Episcopal

Hospital was founded in 1851, the German Hospital (now Lankenau) in 1860, the Jewish Hospital (now Albert Einstein Medical Center—Northern Division) in 1865; the Catholic hospitals of Saint Joseph's in 1849 and Saint Mary in 1860; and Presbyterian Hospital in 1871.

Little provision had been made for the Jews in this area. In 1883-1884 under the leadership of Dr. Joseph B. Potsdamer, chief resident of Jewish Hospital, the Franklin Free Dispensary was established at 322 North Fifth Street, north of Market Street and far out of this area. In 1898, however, the Dispensary opened at 238 Pine Street (now one of the fashionable parts of Society Hill) in a handsome, four-story brick dwelling. There were problems: "the newly graduated immigrant doctors from downtown considered the new dispensary an invasion of their sacred territory by uptown German Jewish doctors," according to Maxwell Whiteman, historian of the Einstein Center.

By August 1899, a group of these downtown doctors organized themselves to establish a sectarian hospital for sick and poor Jews under the name of Beth Israel Hospital. Since Pennsylvania law prohibited the building of a hospital in a heavily populated section of the city, the organizers joined forces with the Franklin Free Dispensary, which retained its name and occupied larger quarters at 236 Pine Street. At this juncture, still another group rose to join them.

In the autumn of 1899, after a door-to-door solicitation in the quarter, the group adopted the name of the Mount Sinai Hospital Association. In April 1900, their zeal was rewarded when all three groups, under the Mount Sinai name, began operation from the Pine Street address. The earliest statistics available are for December 1900, and they tell a dramatic story: there were 1,920 visits to the dispensary; and the pharmacy sold medicine valued at $96.36 and issued 186 prescriptions.

From the beginning, Mount Sinai was a neighborhood hospital, serving the immediate community, not reaching out to other areas of the city as many hospitals did. By 1905, the transition from dispensary to hospital had begun, when a four-story factory building and vacant lot at Fifth and Wilder Streets were purchased. Jacob D. Lit, president of Lit Brothers department store on Market Street, headed a fund-raising committee, which was behind the door-to-door campaign.

The transformation of an abandoned furniture factory into a functioning hospital began in earnest. Before the hospital was officially opened, an emergency case was rushed into the accident ward and the patient was treated in an empty hospital. A week later, on April 11, 1905, Mount Sinai Hospital formally admitted its second patient and a new era in health care was introduced into South Philadelphia. Two of the busiest clinics—surgical and gynecological—set a minimum fee of ten cents! The staff faced not only the problem of ministering to a community in need of medical and surgical care, but one suspicious and fearful of such care—a carry-over from the Old World. The process of overcoming this attitude was long and arduous.

Certain innovations peculiar only to Mount Sinai were developed at the hospital. Trachoma was one of the eye diseases found, with the highest incidence among the immigrant population (if detected upon landing by the immigration authorities, those afflicted were deported). For 20 years, a large number of the 7,000 annual eye cases treated at Mount Sinai had a diagnosis of trachoma.

Most immigrants complained of eye examinations because of the language barrier, so foreign language charts had to be prepared in Russian and Yiddish. There was a certain apathy toward glasses, too, and an absolute refusal to undergo necessary operations. Ways had to be found to overcome these fears and superstitions, and the ingenuity of the hospital staff was often tested.

In 1909, a separate children's department of the hospital was established. A Neuro-Pathological Laboratory was opened soon afterward and a nursing school was started, which then affiliated (1910) with the Jewish Maternity Hospital (established 1873) on Spruce Street. This association lasted 18 years until school and hospital merged with Mount Sinai in 1928.

Expansion was soon necessary—this was obvious not long after the hospital opened—and additional property at Fifth and Reed Streets was acquired. To enlarge the facilities required an even more massive fund-raising effort. Since many of the original families of the area had moved elsewhere as they became more affluent, the campaign was citywide.

The new annex was dedicated in 1911. In 1910 alone—five years after the hospital's opening—Mount Sinai had served 55,659 patients, more than half the population of South Philadelphia east of Broad Street. It had the second busiest dispensary in Philadelphia. By 1919, when it had become a member of the Federation of Jewish Charities, the hospital could report it had treated 56,973 patients in the year ending April 1, 1918.

Drama of a high order occurred in 1922 with the announcement of the discovery of insulin by Frederick G. Banting and Charles H. Best of the University of Toronto. Dr. Albert Salisbury Hyman, Mount Sinai's medical director from 1920 to 1923, proceeded at once to Toronto and successfully obtained six vials (100 cc. each) of the new material. His return journey to Philadelphia was fraught with complications. Dr. Hyman was twice questioned at the frontier by authorities who suspected him of looting the university of its radium supply and again by those who thought he was transporting stolen explosives! A few days after his mission was accomplished, Dr. John B. Deaver, assisted by Dr. Benjamin Lipshutz, successfully removed the leg of a diabetic woman with gangrene in both feet. She had earlier responded to the insulin. It was the first known insulin-controlled amputation in Philadelphia.

In 1952, the name "Albert Einstein Medical Center" was adopted, with Jewish Hospital as the Northern Division and Mount Sinai as the Southern. The designation Daroff Division—in memory of Samuel H. Daroff, a board member and second president of the medical center—was added in 1968. Until 1971, there was talk of closing the hospital, but the community rose as one in opposition. Today the Daroff Division remains a community hospital in an urban center, still playing the same role it set for itself at the beginning of the century.

NAVAL REGIONAL MEDICAL CENTER
17th Street and Pattison Avenue

Located opposite Franklin D. Roosevelt Park and the American-Swedish Historical Museum, the medical center occupies 48 acres on land that was known as New Sweden in the 17th century, before William Penn officially founded the City of Philadelphia. These grounds, too, were part of the area used for the nation's Sesquicentennial Exhibition in 1926, to celebrate the 150th anniversary of independence. The first Navy Yard in the city was in South Philadelphia—farther north at the foot of Federal Street—and the present one lies south of the center at League Island.

In the history of Navy hospitals and health facilities in the Philadelphia area, there have been hospitals at six different locations. During the Revolution, from 1775 until 1782, the pesthouse on Province Island in the Delaware River was used for the care of patients of the Pennsylvania State Navy, except during the British occupation of the city in 1777. However, there was a slight overlap of hospital care from 1779 until the Navy Hospital Fund was established in 1811, when Navy patients by special arrangement were hospitalized at Pennsylvania Hospital. This had its disadvantages. The officers lost control of the patients who were out of sight if not out of jurisdiction, and they often disappeared. It also did not seem proper that officers, seamen and marines should be cared for by a civilian hospital.

There were plans for a naval hospital on Grays Ferry Road along the Schuylkill River, but until that facility was formally acquired, patients were treated in a makeshift building in the Southwark Navy Yard until 1813. After that, a wooden hospital was built at the Navy Yard and used until the move to the Grays Ferry location. The Pemberton mansion was used at the Grays Ferry site until the present Biddle Hall was completed. This property—called the Naval Asylum then—housed a hospital (in three different buildings) until 1921.

The development of the Navy in the 20th century—when the United States emerged as a world power between the close of the Spanish-American War in 1898 and the Armistice of 1918—and the need for larger, more modern facilities made a move imperative. The immediate predecessor of the present center was the League Island Naval Hospital, a temporary wooden structure opened in October 1917 at the Philadelphia Navy Yard. It served this branch of the service until 1935 when the present 13-story hospital was dedicated. During World War I and World War II the Navy hospital received a large number of sick and wounded and after the latter conflict it was developed as a rehabilitation center.

One of the major teaching hospitals of the Navy, it functions as an 800-bed general hospital, with extensive outpatient services, as well as laboratories, medical and dental offices, physical and occupational therapy departments and a pharmacy. Temporary buildings provide beds for additional patients so that the expanded bed capacity of the hospital is listed as 1,750 beds. In an emergency it can be extended to care for approximately 3,000 patients.

The complex is staffed by 250 medical officers, of whom 105 are residents and 34 are interns; 35 Medical Service Corps officers; 170 nurses; and 800 corpsmen.

The present commanding officer of the center, Rear Admiral Robert L. Baker, MC, USN, was the first selection to flag rank of an obstetric-gynecologic specialist on active duty among the armed forces.

NAVAL REGIONAL MEDICAL CENTER

IV WESTWARD

*Philadelphia has always grown westward from its
easternmost boundary, the Delaware River. As William
Penn conceived the city, and as Thomas Holme laid it
out on his map of 1683, Philadelphia stretched through
the wooded areas beyond what is now Broad Street
to the east bank of the Schuylkill River on the west. As
we pursue our quest, we will investigate that area from
Center City on the west side of Broad Street, with a side
trip along the Benjamin Franklin Parkway, and then
proceed to West Philadelphia (University City).*

S. WEIR MITCHELL HOUSE

1524 Walnut Street

A handsome memorial plaque, with a bas-relief by R. Tait McKenzie (a physician-sculptor), was placed here by the Franklin Inn Club, which Dr. Mitchell helped found in 1902 (he was also its first president).

S. Weir Mitchell (1829-1914), called "the most versatile Philadelphian since Benjamin Franklin," lived at this address from 1873 until his death, and it was here that "the best talk in Philadelphia" was heard. While residing here, the doctor-novelist wrote some of his most popular books, among them *Hugh Wynne, Free Quaker* (1896) and *The Red City* (1907), the latter about the crucial years in the final decade of the 18th century, when the Democrats and Federalists were feuding in Philadelphia.

A graduate of Jefferson Medical College (1850), the son of Dr. John Kearsley Mitchell and a collateral descendant of Dr. John Kearsley, Dr. Mitchell was assistant surgeon in the Union army during the Civil War. In this position he had the opportunity to study nerve wounds and diseases of the nervous system. This experience resulted in the publication of *Gunshot Wounds and Other Injuries of the Nerves* (1864), which was amplified and reissued in 1872 as *Injuries of Nerves and Their Consequences*. This work provided an important contribution to knowledge of the peripheral nerves. It was still being used by the French in World War I.

Dr. Mitchell's great contribution was in the study of neuroses — erythromelalgia is referred to as "Mitchell's disease" — and his research (1863-1869) on the physiology of the cerebellum marks him as an experimental investigator of the first rank. *Wear and Tear*, a title which has a contemporary ring to it, concerned the inability or indisposition of Americans to play, and the increase in nervous disorders that were likely to follow — symptoms that also have a modern sound to them. In all, Dr. Mitchell wrote some 119 neurological and 52 pharmacological, physiological and toxicological papers.

Mitchell's "rest cure" made him internationally famous, and despite the controversy aroused by this treatment — healing the mind by restoring the body to health — Weir Mitchell Institutes appeared in France and his technique was applied in England and in Vienna. Even Sigmund Freud adopted a modification of it to combine with his own psychoanalytic therapy.

A practitioner as well as an investigator, Dr. Mitchell was also a man of practicality when it came to treating certain psychological defects. One neurotic Philadelphia matron suffering from a common malaise — despondency — refused to leave her bed when Dr. Mitchell instructed her to do so after the prescribed month of rest was over. He then issued an ultimatum: "Madam, if you are not out of bed in five minutes, I will get in with you."

The story in Philadelphia goes that he began to disrobe, and when he had removed his coat and shoes and his trousers were slipping slowly toward the floor, the patient took him at his word and left her bed immediately. Perhaps Dr. Mitchell's methods were not the accepted ones, but they worked.

F. A. DAVIS COMPANY
1915 Arch Street

A man of sound foresight who ventured south from New England founded this, the third oldest (1879) medical publishing house in the city, and a courageous woman of great strength and purpose took up the reins after his death and succeeded in guiding it successfully through the Depression and the postwar years of World War I and World War II.

Following the Civil War, Frank Allston Davis (1850-1917) left Montpelier, Vermont, and his career of schoolmaster behind him. Coming to Philadelphia, he became a book salesman for a British firm, William Wood and Company, as its exclusive representative in Pennsylvania and New Jersey.

One of those fortunate occurrences that change lives and redirect careers happened to Davis when he was calling on Dr. John V. Shoemaker, dean of the Medico-Chirurgical College (now the Graduate School of Medicine of the University of Pennsylvania). Dr. Shoemaker confided to Davis that he had the manuscript of a book he wished published. That confidence led him to entrust it to Davis and led to the founding of the F. A. Davis Company.

The company grew, but unfortunately Davis developed muscular rheumatism, and his quest for relief took him to St. Petersburg, Florida. In the 28 years following, the company grew and prospered, but not at the rate it might have, because Davis's interests were divided between it and his property and business interests in the Southern resort city.

After his death, his widow, the former Elizabeth Irene Craven (1874-1964), single-handedly managed to salvage the company. One of her more astute moves was to hire Clarence Wilbur Taber as nursing text editor. Taber had been an educational textbook editor for J. B. Lippincott Company in that firm's Chicago office. He applied the principles of his former experience to nursing texts, and established a style for them that other publishers have since followed. He can truthfully be described as the originator of nursing publishing as we know it today. Taber's *Cyclopedic Medical Dictionary*, with total sales over the $3 million mark, and nearly 200,000 copies sold annually, is probably one of the best-selling medical books of all time.

In the archives of the publishing house are the contracts between the Davis Company and Havelock Ellis, of Carbis Water, Lelant, Cornwall, England. One dated 1901 is for *Sexual Inversion* and another dated 1904, for *Sexual Selection in Man*, two of the volumes of his *Studies in the Psychology of Sex*. In 1923, Mrs. Davis sold the rights to these books to Random House. When questioned about the sale by one of the Davis salesmen, she is said to have replied tartly: "Mr. Peterson, this is not a sex house." Following the publication of the "Kinsey Report" by W. B. Saunders Company, *Newsweek* commented on the importance of the study and said that its publication would not have been possible had not the F. A. Davis Company earlier had the courage to publish the Ellis books.

Beginning its existence at 925 Chestnut Street, the firm then moved to 1215 Filbert Street, where it remained until 1901. It then relocated at 1914 Cherry Street just behind its present building, opened in 1969. Robert H. Craven, Mrs. Davis's nephew, became president of the firm in 1960. Under his direction this contemporary headquarters was built — a fitting statement for a progressive publisher about to celebrate its first centenary in business.

THE ACADEMY OF NATURAL SCIENCES OF PHILADELPHIA
19th Street and Benjamin Franklin Parkway

The academy's connection with the medical and pharmaceutical worlds dates from its inception, January 25, 1812, when the founders met at John Speakman's apothecary on the northeast corner of Second and Market Streets. It was "a meeting of gentlemen, friends of science and of rational disposure of leisure moments."

Involved with Speakman in the venture were Dr. Jacob Gilliams, a dentist; Dr. Camillus Macmahon Mann, a physician; Nicholas S. Parmentier, a distiller of whale oil and producer of cordials; Thomas Say, a naturalist and great-nephew of William Bartram, the naturalist; John Shinn, Jr., a manufacturing chemist; and Dr. Gerard Troost, a chemist-pharmacist and later professor at the Philadelphia College of Pharmacy. Thomas Say, "born rich but peculiar," has been described by Nathaniel Burt as: "One of the oddest of its founders....All the elements of Philadelphia's hereditary science might be said to have merged and then been dissipated in him." The academy's name was suggested by Dr. Samuel Jackson, later professor at the University of Pennsylvania. John Barnes, M.D., a botanist, was its first elected member.

As was the case with many of the now-established Philadelphia institutions, the academy began its life in one room—on the second floor of a building on the east side of Second Street near Race. Three years later, it moved to Gilliams Court on Arch Street between Front and Second Streets, and in 1826 it was in a strong enough position financially to purchase the Swedenborgian Church at 12th and George (now Sansom) Streets for its own quarters. By 1836, the List of Members showed that over 30% of the members and 32% of the correspondents were doctors.

The early building that concerns us (the academy's present one has been occupied since about 1875) was on the northwest corner of Broad and Sansom Streets (opposite the Union League). This building was erected in 1839. It was here that the founding meeting of the American Medical Association was held in 1847, with Dr. Nathaniel Chapman of Philadelphia its first elected president.

The collections of the academy—which is devoted to education and environmental research—were impressive from the beginning. In August 1812, John Speakman purchased for it a collection of minerals, the cabinets of Adam Seybert, considered to be the first scientifically trained mineralogist in America. A collection of 1,035 human crania, belonging to Dr. Samuel George Morton, was added later. Dr. Morton's *Crania Americana* (1839) was described as "the most important, extensive and valuable contribution to the natural history of man which has yet appeared on the American continent." Thus began the collections that formed the nucleus of the museum. Today the number of specimens in each category

THE ACADEMY OF NATURAL SCIENCES OF PHILADELPHIA

startles the imagination: 170,000 birds, over a quarter of a million insects, six million shells, a million and a quarter plants, a half-million geological items, two million fish, 30,000 reptiles and amphibians, and 21,000 mammals.

The library evolved similarly. William Maclure, an early benefactor, presented 5,232 volumes (2,259 of these were transported by wagon—often caught in ice floes—from New Harmony, Indiana, in 1835). The library's collections today include 250,000 manuscripts and 150,000 volumes.

Just outside the academy, facing Logan Square and the towers of a new Philadelphia, stands a statue of Dr. Joseph Leidy (1823-1891), elected to membership in 1845 and president of the academy from 1881 to 1891. He was the first American writer in parasitology and vertebrate paleontology and held the chair of anatomy at the University of Pennsylvania's School of Medicine for many years.

The academy, the first and oldest continually operating institution of its kind, is open every day of the year except Thanksgiving, Christmas and New Year's Day: Monday-Saturday, 10:00-5:00; Sunday, 1:00-5:00. Admission: Adults, $1.00; Children and Senior Citizens, $.50. Fees subject to change.

THE COLLEGE OF PHYSICIANS OF PHILADELPHIA
19 South 22nd Street

At its first meeting on January 2, 1787, when the first president, Dr. John Redman, presided, the newly prepared constitution was signed by the Fellows. It ordered "that the institution of the new society should be proclaimed to the world, and that all who are friendly to the progress of medical science should be invited to join in its promotion."

Modeled after the Royal College of Physicians in London, the name "college" was used in the classic sense: a number of persons associated in the pursuit of a common ideal or function. The cause in this case was "to advance the Science of Medicine, and thereby to lessen Human Misery, by investigating the diseases and remedies which are peculiar to our Country:...by cultivating order and uniformity in the practice of Physick."

This, the oldest institution of its kind in the United States, had its first home at Fourth and Arch Streets in the building occupied by the College of Philadelphia (to become the University of Pennsylvania a few years later). Dr. Benjamin Rush, that ubiquitous gentleman whose myriad activities involved him in every aspect of Philadelphia life, read the first scientific paper "On the Means of Promoting Medical Knowledge."

The scientific interests and concerns of the college were varied from the beginning. Soon there were committees appointed to consider the building of hot and cold baths, to plan a botanic garden in the city, to establish a quarantine and a hospital for contagious diseases, and to attempt to arouse general interest in a national pharmacopoeia.

In September 1787, the college advised the Pennsylvania Legislature on the evils of drink. When Congress authorized a 25% excise tax on each gallon of distilled whiskey produced, the Secretary of the Treasury, Alexander Hamilton, read a report from the college stating that the health of Americans would improve with a reduction in their consumption of alcohol.

The illumination of streets when George Washington progressed through Philadelphia on his way to his first inauguration was protested by the Fellows because "the Safety and Comfort of their patients would be imperilled by undue outbursts of patriotism," and the crowds attracted by "a general illumination of the city might be productive of fatal consequences."

Twenty Fellows attended the funeral of Benjamin Franklin on April 21, 1790, and the year following the college moved to Philosophical Hall, the home of Franklin's beloved American Philosophical Society, remaining there until 1845. Later, Governor Mifflin appealed to the college (1799), asking whether it was safe to hold an election in the city because of the yellow fever. He was advised to avoid Southwark, but that the Northern Liberties would be safe.

This involvement in the life of the city continued into the 19th century. In 1824, a special meeting was held in an effort to stay the execution of John Zimmerman, imprisoned in Orwigsburg, Pennsylvania. Zimmerman was under sentence for the murder of his daughter. Two Fellows examined the accused, found him insane, and the execution was denied.

By 1839, the college was advising the Legislature to place public squares with fountains in every district of the city, and in 1843 it suggested the city purchase Lemon Hill mansion to protect the Schuylkill River from contamination (thus beginning Fairmount Park). It disapproved the attempt to patent anesthetic ether under the name "Letheon" (1846), and the next year condemned as an offense the prescribing of medicines by apothecaries. In 1867, the college petitioned the Legislature to legalize dissection. The law doing so (1883) originated in part from this appeal. The college was carrying out the terms of its charter in a positive manner.

As medical knowledge and medical institutions in Philadelphia grew, the importance of the college did also. In 1819, it participated in the successful effort to launch a pharmacopoeia and played a leading role in the decennial revisions thereafter. While the college made successive moves to the Mercantile Library (1845), where the Library Hall now stands, to the "picture house" at Pennsylvania Hospital (1854), to 13th and Locust Streets (1863), and to its present quarters (1909), it achieved a world importance hardly envisioned by its founders.

THE COLLEGE OF PHYSICIANS OF PHILADELPHIA

Never a teaching institution in the ordinary sense, the college is an independent medical society without formal affiliation with any local or national medical school or society. Rather, it is a scientific body dedicated to the reception and discussion of papers on medical, surgical and allied subjects. (These papers are published in the *Transactions & Studies of the College of Physicians of Philadelphia.*)

The library is one of the largest medical libraries in the United States. It has over 10,000 books printed before 1801 (Sir William Osler bequeathed to it a 14th century manuscript of Bernard of Gordon's *Lilium Medicinae*). More than 275,000 volumes, over 325,000 pamphlets and reports, and nearly 3,000 current journals provide a rich source of material for study.

The college's collection of portraits and memorabilia is outstanding. The great of the past gaze down from its walls on those of the present. Here are Drs. John Rhea Barton; Abraham Chovet; Charles Caldwell, Nathaniel Chapman, Robley Dunglison, and Thomas Tickell Hewson by Thomas Sully; Georges Cuvier and Joseph Gay-Lussac by Rembrandt Peale; Plunket Fleeson Glentworth by Gilbert Stuart; Oliver Wendell Holmes; Alexander von Humboldt by Charles Willson Peale; Joseph Leidy and Jacob Da Silva Solis-Cohen.

Clinging tightly to its Philadelphia tradition and sense of history, in 1975 the college honored nearly 200 descendants whose ancestors are represented in the portrait collection. Certain families, such as the Atlees and Woods, still have physicians bearing the name. The tradition of

81

medicine in generation after generation of Philadelphia families is not at all unusual.

The Mütter Museum (begun in 1849) is an unending source of curiosities and memorabilia. The muff Dr. John Foulke carried when he journeyed out to Valley Forge to treat the troops is here, as is his cane; a microscope designed by Oliver Wendell Holmes; the skeleton of the Mütter American Giant (a young man from Kentucky, between 22 and 24 years of age, who was 7' 6"); and several skeletons whose identities are known, such as "Marie Donker, age 29, Domestic, German descent" and "Wilhelm Seiler, German descent, Lithographer, 30 years." There is also the skeleton of one unfortunate maiden whose rib cage was compressed as the result of tight corset lacing, an affliction which has now receded into the mists of time; a display of the labyrinth of the ear of man and all mammalian families, which is superb in its intricacy, detail and completeness; and mementoes of Chang and Eng Bunker, the Siamese twins who died in 1874. There is no other museum quite like it in Philadelphia or, perhaps, the world.

The visitor should not fail to linger outside in the Medicinal Herb Garden, an oasis in the heart of the city, which was originally suggested to the Fellows by Dr. Benjamin Rush almost two centuries ago. The patterned herb beds, the trees and the ivy, the charming statue by Edward Fenno Hoffman, and the sense of serenity all this imparts entices the wayfarer to tarry.

Following its original precepts of involving itself in the current of the times, the college has shown every evidence of being up-to-the-minute. In 1972, the Fellows elected Dr. Katharine R. Boucot Sturgis as president, the first woman in its history to hold the office. Now, 189 years after its founding, the college looks forward to entering its third century. Its motto incised over the entrance—*Non Sibi Sed Toti* (Not for one's self but for all)— reflects its achievement more than a chronicle of its past and present accomplishments could.

The college is usually open Monday-Friday, 9:00-5:00. Museum hours during the Bicentennial year may vary and be expanded. They can be ascertained by calling (215) 561-6050, Extension 41.

PHILADELPHIA GENERAL HOSPITAL
700 Civic Center Boulevard

There has been a controversy in Philadelphia medical circles for well over 200 years—and arguments do not die easily in Philadelphia—about whether the Philadelphia General Hospital or the Pennsylvania Hospital is the oldest in the city, and, by reason of this, the oldest in the nation. By definition, Pennsylvania Hospital (founded 1751) is the oldest because it was founded as a *hospital* by Benjamin Franklin and Dr. Thomas Bond. But almost 40 years earlier (1712), when Philadelphia as a city was only 30 years old, an almshouse was proposed. It was not until 1728, however, that money was appropriated for it. The almshouse was finally erected in 1732 (the year construction on the State House, or Independence Hall, began). Earlier in the same year, George Washington was born in Westmoreland County, Virginia.

Situated on the block between Spruce and Pine, Third and Fourth Streets, the site was familiarly known as Almshouse Square. The official opening date was December 6, 1732. The "first to provide public support for medical care to its citizens," the almshouse remained on the edge of Society Hill in the Old City until 1767. It was noted in the Colonial records of Pennsylvania as early as 1734 that "a sober and discreet person [is] to reside at the Almshouse to care for the Poor therin [sic]."

It *was* an almshouse: "...the first place in Philadelphia to which the poor and the sick, the unfortunate girl and the unemployed, the aged and the insane could go, was the Philadelphia Almshouse, now known as the Philadelphia General Hospital." But it was much more — a lying-in hospital, a foundling hospital for infants, a place where the insane were cared for humanely. The demands on it were great, and between 1760 and 1766, a tract for a new home was purchased between 10th and 11th Streets, Spruce to Pine. The following year, the 284 inmates were transferred to the then-rural district to the west. During this period, Dr. William Shippen (the elder) was thought to be the first doctor connected with the almshouse; Dr. Benjamin Rush was on the staff of the infirmary from 1774 to 1777. Dr. Thomas Bond, with Dr. Cadwalader Evans, "was evidently giving lectures on obstetrics in the wards of the Almshouse to his students before January 3, 1771."

We discover that by 1775 it was a "Hospital for Curables and Incurables of all ages and sexes, and in every disease and malady, even to Lunacy and Idiotism to a considerable degree...." The Revolution, which brought changes to every segment of the city's life, was felt within the walls of the almshouse. In the minutes of the almshouse for February 2, 1776, we find mention that soldiers were sent there until Congress could make provision for them. "On November 19, 1776, sick and wounded soldiers were cared for at the Bettering House, as the Almshouse was colloquially called." Thomas Wharton, Jr., the president of the Council of Safety, requested quarters there for Continental soldiers suffering from dysentery in September of that year. The following month, Dr. William Shippen, Jr., Director-General of the Hospital of the Continental army, ordered the almshouse cleared of the poor and the sick and the Continental soldiers brought in.

Records before the Revolution are scarce; earlier ones were irretrievably lost. But they were, fortunately, preserved during the formative years of the young Republic. We learn that John Trust was appointed apothecary to the almshouse in 1788. He was also to attend to ward dressings, keep records of admissions and diagnoses and accounts of deliveries. In return for his services, John received board, lodging and laundry. No mention was made of hard currency. A clinic for students was established in the obstetrical department as early as 1770. Soon afterward, medical and surgical lectures and the opening of the wards to non-resident pupils, and to resident physicians, extended the teaching program of the almshouse.

In 1828, as the city continued to grow and extend itself to the west, the board of trustees looked westward, too. Ground was purchased in the village of Blockley, which was part of the 1,500 acres purchased from the Indians by William Warner in 1677 before the arrival of William Penn. It was named for Warner's native parish in Warwickshire. The new hospital, with "its long wings, its gloomy walls, its portico held up by Grecian pillars," was remembered with fondness years later by Dr. J. Chalmers Da Costa.

"Blockley," as it was known, lay across the Schuylkill River, facing the United States Naval Hospital at Grays Ferry. The students from the University of Pennsylvania and Jefferson Medical College reached it by jamming into horsecars and riding either to the South Street ferry or the wooden bridge over Market Street. "So important had grown the clinical instruction at Blockley that in 1834 both Jefferson and Pennsylvania were approached with the proposal that they require house tickets to Blockley as prerequisites for graduation." (Student tickets sold for eight dollars and for some years there was an added fee of three or four dollars charged for a certificate of attendance.) Neither school ratified this proposal. In 1835, the name was changed to the Philadelphia Hospital, but Blockley remained the popular name, especially among the early personnel and the residents of the area.

Blockley, too, was in advance of its time. "Women in medicine may date their first recognition at the Almshouse to July 1, 1810; for at that time a Mrs. Lavender was made assistant mid wife 'in order the better to perfect her education.' Regular practitioners of medicine among women were denied recognition for many years." Sarah Adamson applied to the board in 1851 for "such a situation in the Blockley hospital as will afford me an opportunity of seeing its practice to such an extent and under such conditions as may comfort [sic] with the proper regulations of the institution." Her appeal was made in the year following the establishment of The Female Medical College of Pennsylvania (later The Woman's Medical College, now The Medical College of Pennsylvania). The hospital's committee requested the chief resident physician to "assign her to such position as will best enable her to obtain the knowledge she desires without detriment to the institution." In 1868-1869, women students first attended the general clinical lectures. However, not until October 1882 did Clara Marshall become visiting physician to Blockley, delivering clinical lectures to mixed classes. (She also held ward classes for her own students of The Woman's Medical

PHILADELPHIA GENERAL HOSPITAL

College as well as for private pupils.) The next year, when the first competitive examinations were held for the residencies at Blockley, placing sixth among the twelve candidates was Mary Pauline Root, a graduate of The Woman's Medical College – the first woman resident.

Once established, Blockley firmly took its place in the Philadelphia medical community. Three specialty departments – neurological, ophthalmological and dermatological – were added in 1877. Dr. William Osler declared when coming to Philadelphia from Montreal in 1884 "that not the least of the reasons for his coming was the promise of a position on the Blockley staff." A photograph of Osler's pathological seminar in 1887 shows 18 people surrounding two cadavers of uncertain condition and certainly the worse for wear. The men all wear caps or derbies and white aprons over their suits. The only uncovered, unaproned figure is that of Amelia Gilman! (Resident physicians wore a blue uniform with brass buttons and braid, patterned after that of a surgeon in the United States Navy, and a cloth cap with a stiff visor and a soft top.)

Nursing training came to Blockley in 1884 with the arrival of Miss Alice Fisher, chief nurse of the Birmingham, England, Hospital, and her assistant Miss Edith Horner. Actually, George W. Childs, the Philadelphia publisher, asked an English intermediary to consult Florence Nightingale, the heroine of the Crimean War, over the choice. Miss Nightingale selected Miss Fisher. Classes began in January 1885; a year later, the first class – 15 in number – graduated. Before Miss Fisher's time, nurses were hired when a

85

need arose and acquired what knowledge they had as they went along.

It could be said just before the turn of the century that "all the masters of Clinical Medicine in Philadelphia with [Alfred] Stillé and [J. Chalmers] Da Costa drew the portraits of disease from a never-failing wealth of material [at Blockley]." Clinical lectures always had an uphill battle at Blockley. In 1845, following a dispute, Blockley closed as a clinical school for nine years. Reopening, it was the scene of lectures attended by the city's medical students, and by 1892, Dr. Roland Curtin could say: "I have made a calculation that in 31 years fifteen to twenty thousand students have attended clinics in the old Clinic rooms."

In 1902, the name was again changed from the Philadelphia Hospital to the Philadelphia General Hospital; in 1919, the first outpatient clinic (genitourinary) was established; in 1920, the almshouse designation was eliminated when there was a transfer of occupants to the Home for the Indigent. By 1926, the final transfer of the mentally disturbed to the Philadelphia State Hospital at Byberry was accomplished. This was a prelude to the new hospital buildings in 1927 — the hospital as we know it today. In that year, the outpatient clinics had increased to 15.

Today the Philadelphia General Hospital is the only public hospital in the city of Philadelphia (and the oldest public hospital in continual existence in the United States).

PHILADELPHIA CHILD GUIDANCE CLINIC
34th Street and Civic Center Boulevard

Established in 1925 as the All-Philadelphia Child Guidance Clinic — the last of seven Commonwealth Demonstration Clinics established by the Commonwealth Fund of New York and the National Committee for Mental Hygiene — the Philadelphia Child Guidance Clinic has in 50 years revolutionized the concept of treating emotionally disturbed children. It was the first clinic in the United States in which the psychiatric, psychological and social approaches to mental health were combined and today serves the five-county Greater Philadelphia community.

For two years, it operated as a demonstration clinic, but from the beginning those associated with it recognized that it must be a permanent facility. They were abetted in their conviction by many prominent Philadelphians who realized the staff was furrowing a hitherto fallow field. In every sense, the facility was a pioneering one. Goldie Basch Faith, one of its original social workers, recalled: "There was lacking any sufficient body of literature, and theories about such matters as early child-mother relationships, the effects of early deprivation, or parent-child separations were at their most elementary beginnings."

In 1925, when the clinic opened its doors in a converted house at 1711 Fitzwater Street, the child psychologist did not exist in any recognizable form. The only psychiatrists in Philadelphia with any "training" in working with children, other than regular training in general psychiatry, were in the Philadelphia Child Guidance Clinic. "There was no practicing psychoanalyst in Philadelphia. A few individuals had gone to New York for analyses," according to Dorothy Hankins, M.S.W., historian of the clinic.

Dr. Frederick H. Allen, "who seemed to be a man born to help children," served as director from 1925 to 1956. He was remembered by one colleague as "more completely at home with himself than anyone else I have ever known; the result was that his energies were almost fully available for productive purposes." When asked what he and Miss Almena Dawley, Chief Social Worker, had in common, he replied: "Our ignorance and our determination to learn how to help children and their parents. That was what all the staff had in common in the beginning."

They met resistance from certain religious groups and members of the judiciary, but, by and large, once the doors opened the clinic's importance was immediately apparent. Philadelphia had long been recognized as an outstanding neurological center, and its Mental Hygiene Committee in the Public Charities Association of Pennsylvania was one of the most active in the country. It offered an inviting opportunity to develop still further the community participation and cooperation needed in the evolution of child guidance.

As of May 1, 1927, when diagnostic and functional social work had not been heard of, some 668 children had been studied—an impressive figure in two short years—and the "transition from a demonstration to a permanent clinic with local control and responsibility had gone remarkably smoothly." Relationships with public and private educational institutions and with many of the health and welfare organizations were also progressing well.

The concept of the child in the family system, with focus on the interrelationships of parents and child, dictated to the staff that whatever was done with one member of the family had to be done within the context of the whole. This concept is the essence of family therapy, and is germane to the clinic's methodology. "A willingness to consider the possibility that parents were right and the professionals wrong seems to have been characteristic of Dr. Allen from the beginning," as was the collaboration of the psychiatrist, the psychologist and the social worker at the clinic itself.

By the mid-1930's, the staff had assimilated the concept of the issue being the interrelationship among child, parents and situation, and though the child was referred to as the patient, Dr. Allen made little use of the medical analogy. He and the clinic were seen as "anti-Freudian and were openly spoken of as 'Rankian.'" (Dr. Allen did arrange with Dr. Otto Rank and the Pennsylvania School of Social Work to have Rank give a seminar on therapeutic issues to the clinical staff.)

In 1953, a new facility was opened at 17th and Bainbridge Streets, adjacent to The Children's Hospital of Philadelphia, the clinic's major medical affiliate since the beginning. This remained the clinic's home until the present structure, this time adjoining Children's Hospital, was dedicated on May 6, 1974. HRH Princess Margaret of Great Britain and her husband, the Earl of Snowdon, came from London to assist Dr. Salvador Minuchin, the clinic's third director, and his staff in the opening ceremonies. Interestingly enough, many years before, Mrs Amy Strachey, an English-woman, paid the hospital a visit while in Philadelphia. As a result of this, she helped found the first child guidance centers in the British Isles.

Today, the clinic provides outpatient services (2,761 patients in fiscal 1975) at three service locations and a short-term intramural program of inpatient care and of psychoeducationally oriented day treatment. It is a major center for training of Fellows in child psychiatry, social workers, clinical psychologists and family counselors, and for general training in family therapy.

It is recognized as one of the nation's pioneers in the development of therapeutic and preventive child psychiatry, and a foremost child psychiatry agency with a family slant. It has also pioneered in the development of the community clinic concept, supporting a policy of service to patients from all socioeconomic levels, especially the lower ones, and it has been an innovator in dealing with psychosomatic problems in collaboration with Children's Hospital.

THE CHILDREN'S HOSPITAL OF PHILADELPHIA

34th Street and Civic Center Boulevard

In examining that special time known as childhood, Eleanor Farjeon, who achieved fame as a writer for children, said that childhood is a lifetime of its own, complete as a life of sixty or ninety years might be. When she expressed this theory, it was not one accepted generally.

Eighty years before, in 1855, it was less so. The situation of children was far from a fortunate one. In that era the growth and development of children was of negligible interest. Immigration was beginning to accelerate, and in every large city thousands of poor children lived in cheerless, airless tenements or overcrowded houses, ill-fed and plagued by disease and neglect. The time was appropriate for founding The Children's Hospital of

Philadelphia, the first on the North American continent and consequently the oldest in the United States. Founded as a charity hospital, its first home was a modest dwelling on Blight Street (now Watts).

As in the founding of all Philadelphia hospitals, the men who conceived Children's Hospital were dedicated people, possessed of vision. Francis West Lewis, Thomas Hewson Bache (a great-great-grandson of Benjamin Franklin) and R.A.F. Penrose announced their intention to Philadelphians through the columns of the *Public Ledger* on November 23, 1855:

> The Children's Hospital—located on Blight Street, running from Pine to Lombard, below Broad, is now open for the reception of Patients. Children suffering from Acute Diseases and Accidents will be received free of charge. A Dispensary, for sick children, is also attached to the Hospital and will be open at the same place every day, (Sundays excepted) from 11 to 12 o'clock, when advice and medicines will be given free of charge.

This simple declaration of purpose was to change child care in America and has been rightly called "the dawn of pediatrics in the United States."

Dr. Lewis was inspired by a visit to the Hospital for Sick Children—the first of its kind in the English-speaking world—in London. His response was an indication of the forward-looking attitude of the Philadelphia medical community at a time when the profession was often plagued by ignorance and quackery.

By 1866, the growth, and the demand for admittance, was great enough to necessitate larger quarters. They were found in a commodious brownstone dwelling on South 22nd Street, between Walnut and Locust Streets (where the English Village now stands). It had accommodations for 35 children (increased to 94 in 1892), and a dispensary. It was to be Children's Hospital for the next half-century.

Once established—the hospital was never a pesthouse or an asylum for poor children, but a hospital devoted to clinical care—it was not long before the introduction of other specialties began: surgery in 1870; a clinic for eye treatment and diseases of the ear in 1873; one for the nose and throat in 1892; and the addition of a pathologist in 1893 and a laryngologist five years later.

Other remarkable men distinguished the formative years. John Forsyth Meigs, an obstetrician and a member of the consulting staff from 1855 to 1882, made significant contributions to infant feeding and the nutritional disturbances of infancy. His son Arthur Vincent Meigs, a member of the outpatient department and a founder of the American Pediatric Society, had a special interest in infant feeding (reflecting the incidence of, and high infant mortality from, diarrhea), which resulted in *Milk Analysis and Infant Feeding*, considered a pediatric classic.

John Price Crozer Griffith investigated inflammation of the divertic-

THE CHILDREN'S HOSPITAL OF PHILADELPHIA

ulum in childhood (Meckel's diverticulum). In 1893, Dr. Alfred Hand "was the first to record before the American Pediatric Society what is now known as the Hand-Christian-Schüller syndrome" (now placed among the lipoid diseases). Howard Childs Carpenter, who joined the dispensary staff in 1904, became director of the Department for the Prevention of Diseases in 1914, "the first such department to be established in any hospital in the nation, setting forth concern for well children as a new concept." Dr. Carpenter believed "the ideal children's hospital would minister not only to the illnesses of infants and children but to the 'entire child,' his physical and mental health and development, but also to prophylaxis against disease, broad concepts now embodied in the program of most children's medical centers."

In 1911, Dr. Samuel McC. Hamill reopened a summer department of the hospital for the care and study of infant diarrhea. At that time Children's Hospital had no accommodations for infants up to two years, and Dr. Hamill suggested the idea of a hospital for babies, which was later built at Seventh and Delancey Streets, not far from Pennsylvania Hospital.

Early in this century, a number of specialty clinics had either been initiated or developed in the outpatient department of the hospital: a consulting neurologist was named in 1914; an anesthetist the following year; a consulting orthopedist in 1917 and an orthopedic surgeon in 1918.

A move was again needed; larger quarters were a necessity. In 1909, property was purchased on 18th Street, extending from Bainbridge to

90

Fitzwater, but the actual relocation did not take place until 1916. In 1921-1922, a second unit was added, giving a bed capacity of 85.

When Dr. Joseph Stokes, Jr., was appointed acting chairman of the pediatrics department and acting physician-in-chief of Children's Hospital in 1929, that year was considered the hospital's entry into the modern era, just as the founding of the hospital had been considered the dawn of pediatrics. Dr. Stokes recalled the ambitions of Dr. John Gittings (professor of pediatrics at the University of Pennsylvania) for the wider development of the hospital as an educational institution, and for the more thorough application of modern methods of teaching and investigation. Stokes gathered about him a gifted group of young clinicians and investigators. During the 34 years of his tenure, the hospital became one of the foremost pediatric centers of the country.

There was a strong affiliation from the beginning with the other hospitals and medical schools of the city. The first three attending physicians, who were also founders, had served their residencies at Pennsylvania Hospital. From its founding, Children's Hospital always had a close, practical relationship with the School of Medicine of the University of Pennsylvania. With a long tradition as an academic teaching institution, Children's Hospital has always involved the student in actual clinical experience. In 1877, the hospital medical and surgical clinics were "made accessible to students without charge, and owing to the thorough nature of the instructions given and the convenient location of the Hospital...well attended and popular." By 1893, the popularity of the clinical lectures — both medical and surgical — was such that the facilities had to be expanded. By now, pediatrics was recognized as a science apart from medicine in general and separated from obstetrics and the diseases of women. Clinical teaching at the bedside — reminiscent of the earlier instruction in the amphitheatre when the surgeon lectured as he operated — became part of the program. When, in 1930, the professor of pediatrics at the University of Pennsylvania became physician-in-chief of Children's Hospital, and members of the hospital's pediatric staff held teaching posts at the university, this action assured Children's Hospital of continued status as a major teaching institution (there had been a formal affiliation with the University of Pennsylvania since 1919). There is also a reciprocal residency exchange program between the Hospital for Sick Children in London and a training relationship with the American Research Hospital for Children in Krakow, Poland.

In the area of research, the hospital first focused on pathology, clinical medicine and the development of surgical techniques; later, upon nutrition and attention to the bearing of nutrition and hygiene upon child health. The interest here was on "the whole child," which was reflected as the years passed in the quality and extent of research. In the 1940's, the hospital's major emphasis on bacteriology, virology and viral diagnosis was to bring it worldwide acclaim. It was recognized for its many contributions in immunology and epidemiology; for its major contributions in the area of nephritis and nephrosis; for the development of the "Isolette" incubator; and clinical application of ultraviolet light as a means of reducing airborne infection; for work on Rh problems; and for a growing appreciation of integration between somatic and emotional problems, and for collaborative therapy developed by psychiatrists and pediatricians. In 1954, a new research building was dedicated, and by the advent of the 1960's, Children's Hospital achieved and has since maintained one of the largest pediatric research budgets in the world.

As a seasoned vintner would say: "1974 was a very good year." In that year, the hospital relocated a fourth time, to its present magnificent new facility — built at a cost of $80 million — which it shares with the Philadelphia Child Guidance Clinic. In this new home in September of 1974, an operation was performed that captured the sympathy of the world. Dr. C. Everett Koop, surgeon-in-chief, and a specially selected team of 23 surgeons, nurses, anesthetists and technicians operated successfully on Siamese twins. The sisters Clara and Altagracia Rodriguez had been flown to Philadelphia from their home in the Dominican Republic. The 10-1/2 hour operation, which severed the two bodies and reconstructed vital organs in each, caught the world unaware. Planning and rehearsals had gone on for days in secret. The miracle had been accomplished: the children lived, responded and thrived. Almost 12 decades after a simple declaration of intent appeared in the *Public Ledger* that the Children's Hospital "is now open....Children suffering from Acute Diseases and Accidents will be received free of charge," another great accomplishment became part of the history of this world-famous hospital.

HOSPITAL OF THE UNIVERSITY OF PENNSYLVANIA
34th and Spruce Streets

Opened in 1874, the hospital has served several million patients since it was founded as the first general hospital in the United States expressly designed and built by a university to provide bedside teaching facilities for its medical school.

The hospital had its genesis in 1871, when Dr. William Pepper, Jr. (later provost of the university), Dr. Horatio C. Wood and Dr. William F. Norris all saw the need for an effective relationship between the lecture rooms and the hospital wards. This, almost on the eve of the university's move from Ninth Street to West Philadelphia, was partially due to geog-

92

raphy: the School of Medicine had used Pennsylvania Hospital for clinical teaching while in the Old City. But that would no longer be practical because of the distance between the new campus and the hospital. The following year, the medical alumni met and agreed that a hospital was a necessity; the university board of trustees agreed to set aside land on campus for it.

A drive for $700,000—a modest sum by today's standards—was launched with Isaiah Williamson giving $50,000 (in all $140,000 was raised by contribution) and the state giving $200,000. The state later gave an additional $100,000. In 1872, the City of Philadelphia granted the university an additional five and one-half acres, and the hospital was almost an actuality.

The first building was three stories high, accommodating 146 beds (it was planned to be a 600-bed facility eventually), and opened on July 15, 1874. The first patient, Carris Davis, was admitted on July 27, to be followed by John French the next day.

As in many hospitals at that time, by early 1875 the hospital was facing financial difficulty, and the board of managers found it necessary to request the medical staff to consider reducing the nursing staff and other departments. Even so, ground was broken in 1881 for the Gibson Building— a wing for chronic diseases that opened in 1883 with 63 additional beds, increasing the hospital capacity to over 200. (It reached 350 beds in 1897.) The new building also provided for a separation of medical and surgical cases—something long deemed desirable, but not formerly possible.

The need for a nursing school had been felt from the beginning (William Pepper had suggested a nurses training school in 1874), and the matter had been debated and considered for some time. From 1874 to 1882, only one nurse was assigned to each ward; thereafter there were two. Finally, Charlotte Marie Hugo, an Englishwoman, was named superintendent in 1886, and the nursing school opened in December, offering a two-year course of study. This was at the time that Miss Alice Fisher, also from England, was setting up nurses training nearby at the Philadelphia Hospital (Blockley). Miss Hugo was more than a superintendent and directress of nursing. She was a woman of all work: business manager, purchasing agent, personnel administrator and dietitian as well.

The growth of the school was rapid, due in great part to the advantage of having the School of Medicine and the hospital as departments of the university. A maternity ward was added in 1888, but housed in a separate building on the grounds, and there were individual accommodations for five patients at a time. At the year's end in 1889, the hospital reported 42,789 days of patient care, with the average length of stay 30 days.

The 1890's saw tremendous strides forward at the hospital: the addition of a pathology building in 1890, as well as a children's orthopedic ward, the construction of the Pepper Laboratory of Clinical Medicine (1894), the $160,000 Agnew Memorial Pavilion (1897) and, perhaps most important of all, the Roentgen Laboratory in 1896. Charles Lester Leonard read his first paper on X ray only a few months after Wilhelm C. Roentgen announced his discovery in Germany. Leonard assembled necessary electrical equipment and purchased an X-ray tube. He began assisting surgeons by taking radiographs of the extremities of the body and also by studying the use of the X ray in diagnosis and therapy. Dr. Henry Pancoast joined Leonard several years later and eventually succeeded him.

The turn of the century was at hand. In 1898, the first inpatient student health unit—with a special ward of 10 beds—opened to accommodate university students. That same year, with the outbreak of hostilities in the Spanish-American War, trainloads of surgical attendants and supplies were dispatched at the hospital's expense to military camps in the East and the South. Later, 267 soldiers were admitted to the hospital. Of 145 with typhoid fever, only five died. Typhoid was an ever-present danger, and when the hospital reported 75,876 days of care provided in 1902—an increase of 7,308 over the previous year—it attributed the rise to a large number of typhoid and pneumonia cases treated that year.

Two important departments were organized in the years preceding World War I: the Social Service Department in 1907 and the Department of Physical Therapy in 1911. Accommodations were made to the war itself. In 1915, Dr. J. William White (who retired as chief of surgery in 1910) accompanied a team of physicians and nurses to Paris, where they were to help care for Allied troops. The war took its toll in many ways. In 1918—the year of the Armistice—73 staff nurses left the hospital for positions in the services. That year also saw the influenza epidemic that demoralized the nation. The hospital managed to survive through the efforts of Dr. Alfred Stengel, chief of medicine, and a young chief resident, Isidor S. Ravdin, who had just begun his duties, but who would one day be one of the most important medical men in America. In 1920, the remarkable Dr. Chevalier Jackson occupied the newly established chair of bronchology and esophagology. (At various times he was also associated with other medical schools of the city.)

When the hospital reached its half-century mark in 1924, it could report for that year 9,100 inpatients, 6,638 operations performed and 18,771 outpatients. In 1927, Edmund B. Piper was made chief of obstetrics. Among other distinctions, he served as the model for the doctor-protagonist in the novel *Take These Hands* by Anne Paterson (Anne Einselen), which became an overnight best seller in Philadelphia in 1939.

Since that time, the chronology of achievement has been more rapid than ever. The 698-bed hospital's physical plant now dominates the corner of 34th Street and the south side of Spruce Street—the Thomas Sovereign Gates Pavilion for outpatient clinics, the George Morris Piersol Rehabilitation Center, the William H. Donner Center for Radiology, the I. S. Ravdin

Institute for surgical and medical patient care and research. The newest addition will be the 14-level glass and concrete Louis Silverstein Pavilion facing 34th Street and connecting with the Ravdin Institute. It will cost approximately $40 million and will include five floors of inpatient units, a cancer research and treatment center, four floors of physicians' offices, and an expanded emergency facility, among other features. It should be ready for occupancy in 1978.

Among the recent medical developments for which the hospital is noted is the exchange transfusion treatment for infants with hyaline membrane disease (the infant's blood is exchanged for fresh adult blood), which has a 70% survival rate. The Multiple Sclerosis Center is one of five established nationally for research and treatment; the Neurological Intensive Care Unit is also one of five head injury clinical centers in the nation sponsored for advanced treatment and research by the National Institutes of Health. A Surgical Intensive Care Unit for cardiothoracic surgery is unique, with its computerized monitoring system that gives a reading of body functions every 60 seconds. It can begin transfusions automatically. The computer monitor is principally for open heart surgery patients (the hospital has 300-400 annually) and is supported by a grant in excess of $350,000 from the National Institutes of Health. The hospital's lung bypass equipment (one of nine centers in the country) shared a $6 million grant from the National Heart and Lung Institute. This equipment can support the lungs during acute respiratory insufficiency (which claims 60,000 victims a year) by providing oxygenation of the blood.

HOSPITAL OF THE UNIVERSITY OF PENNSYLVANIA

SCHOOL OF MEDICINE OF THE UNIVERSITY OF PENNSYLVANIA

Hamilton Walk

It was the Age of Enlightenment even in the Colonies scattered along the Atlantic coast. Almost every man of education in the 18th century had some acquaintance with, if not knowledge of, medicine. Those families of means whose sons desired to study medicine sent them to London, Leyden, Paris or Edinburgh. Most Philadelphians journeyed to Edinburgh, the Athens of the North.

"London hospital practice without Edinburgh lectures was, in the old analogy, like going to sea without having studied navigation; while to attend lectures in the Scottish university but never do practical anatomical and clinical work of the kind which London offered was like not going to sea at all," according to Whitfield J. Bell, Jr., historian of early American medicine. The University of Edinburgh is rightly considered the "mother" institution of the School of Medicine of the University of Pennsylvania and the Scotch thistle mounted over the entrance to the school symbolizes the bond.

Two of these young Colonials—John Morgan and William Shippen, Jr. —were friends at the time they studied in London and the Scottish capital, but fell out when the medical school, the first in America, was founded in 1765. It is generally agreed that Shippen had the idea first, but Morgan, an ambitious young man fresh from the grand tour (including a visit with Voltaire) and filled with the desire of "transplanting medical science" into the Colonies, delivered his "Discourse Upon the Institution of Medical Schools in America," and the die was cast. The trustees of the College of Philadelphia adopted his plan, and Morgan had the honor of being appointed the first medical professor on the faculty. Shippen, Adam Kuhn and Benjamin Rush joined him soon afterward—"probably the youngest faculty that ever sat in professors' chairs." The new school, modeled after that of Edinburgh, occupied rooms in the College of Philadelphia at Fourth and Arch Streets, with Morgan teaching "theory and practice of physick," Shippen anatomy and surgery, Rush chemistry, and Kuhn botany and materia medica.

"Morgan's plan, in fact, comprised practically all the elements of medical instruction that after long, costly trial and error the American profession has since found to be essential," according to George W. Corner, M.D., historian of the School of Medicine.

Ten young men graduated in the first class (1768), receiving the degree of Bachelor of Medicine. (Doctor of Medicine was only awarded to those with three years' professional experience who had also submitted a thesis in Latin. By 1791, all graduates received M.D. degrees.)

It has been said that the most important event in the life of those born in 1755 who became physicians was the American Revolution. In fact, Colonel Fielding H. Garrison declared it was "the making of medicine in this country." The Revolution made inroads in the life of the school: there were no graduates in 1774 or any subsequent year until 1780 and, except for 1777-1778, the courses were much shortened. Morgan, Rush and Shippen were all members of Washington's army.

As the Age of Enlightenment drew to its close, the medical school began its post-Revolution growth. There was a troubled time in the 1780's when the College of Philadelphia split into rival factions (the University of the State of Pennsylvania was the other), but they finally settled their differences and merged as the University of Pennsylvania—the first institution of higher learning to adopt the title of university in the United States.

The President's House on Ninth Street between Chestnut and Market—which neither Presidents Washington nor Adams occupied—became the medical school's home in 1802, remaining so until it was demolished in 1829. (The new buildings that were erected formed the campus of the university from that year until 1872.) Three years later, a separate chair of surgery—as distinct from medicine—was created for Philip Syng Physick. Surgery, anatomy and obstetrics prior to that had been united in one chair. "It was thus that surgery rose to its legitimate position earlier in Philadelphia than in Edinburgh."

Those whom we recognize as the giants of medicine in the past joined Physick at the medical school. Benjamin Smith Barton, who published America's first textbook on botany, succeeded Benjamin Rush as professor of theory and practice of medicine in 1813, only to be succeeded by Nathaniel Chapman three years later. Others include James Woodhouse, who more than anyone else, except Lavoisier, helped to establish the existence of oxygen; Caspar Wistar in anatomy; and Joseph Leidy, America's foremost comparative anatomist.

In 1825, a year after the founding of Jefferson Medical School (the second in Philadelphia), there were about a dozen medical schools in the country, many of them proprietary schools without academic ties or standards. The university's School of Medicine was teaching one fifth of the nation's medical students, among them a large number of Southerners (especially in the years 1819-1835). By the mid-1840's, there were about 35 medical schools in the United States, but the mortality rate among them was great.

Medical education in the early and mid-19th century was conducted differently than it is today. Professors holding chairs at the medical school were paid fees directly by the students, rather than receiving a salary from the university. They, in turn, made an annual payment to the university for the use of the medical hall, so that medical teaching was a private enterprise under university teaching. In 1859, the trustees released the faculty from payment of taxes and from the incoming professors' assessment. (It was not until 1876 that the question of salaries was resolved, with fixed salaries being paid by the university.)

Following the raid of John Brown at Harpers Ferry, West Virginia, in 1859, some 180 southern students at Jefferson Medical School and 18 at the university's school hurriedly left Philadelphia for the Medical College of Virginia at Richmond. More than 1,700 graduates of the university's School of Medicine—25% of the Confederate army surgeons and 6% of the Union's —served in the Civil War. During this period (1864), George Bacon Wood persuaded the trustees and the faculty that the curriculum must be broadened and natural science brought back. (Mathematics and natural philosophy—physics—had been dropped in 1789, botany in 1813.) Wood's nephew Horatio C. Wood was the author of a textbook on therapeutics that was credited "with having done more than any other single work to put modern American therapeutics on a scientific basis."

Brilliant European scientists—Pasteur, Koch and Lister among them —were changing the face of medicine. The discovery of asepsis was revolutionizing treatment, as was modern pharmacology. In line with the new wave of discovery in medicine, the school emerged from the traditions of the past. Following an increasing Philadelphia trend, the university moved across the Schuylkill River to West Philadelphia in 1872. Two years later the Hospital of the University of Pennsylvania was established, making bedside teaching an essential part of education at the school and contributing notably to the late 19th century reform in medical education.

Standards of fitness were strengthened for admission to the school in 1880, with the elevation of the reformer Dr. William Pepper, Jr., as provost in 1881. (At that time, the provost was the chief executive officer.) It was he who conceived of the hospital and energetically promoted its establishment.

Gynecology became a department of its own in 1874, when William Goodell was given charge of clinical diseases of women and children. (Obstetrics had been a separate department since 1810.) Pediatrics received academic recognition in 1884, and John P. C. Griffith, clinical professor of pediatrics, was later the author of The Care of the Infant, which went into six editions between 1895 and 1923.

William Osler was named professor of medicine in 1884, remaining until he was called to Baltimore to be one of the four founding members of Johns Hopkins University Medical School. D. Hayes Agnew, celebrated in Thomas Eakins's painting, "The Agnew Clinic," which hangs in the School of Medicine today, joined the faculty in 1870 as professor of surgery. He was one of the first surgeons to adopt asepsis in the operating room. The School of Dental Medicine was established in 1878. (Today it is known for its broad medical approach to dentistry and its definition of this specialty, which the World Health Organization has adopted.)

Enrollment reached a high point in 1893, when it totaled 793. That same year, Provost Pepper emphasized practical instruction at the bedside and in laboratories for every student and the course of study became a four-year one. In the autumn of 1897, when the first class under this new order began its senior year, there were four full classes in attendance and enrollment reached 926. Two years later, Simon Flexner accepted the chair of pathology, remaining until 1903, when he joined the Rockefeller Institute in New York.

William F. Norris was the first to occupy the chair of ophthalmology, followed by George E. de Schweinitz. Charles Krasner Mills, who accepted the chair of neurology in 1903, had been a witness at the trial of Charles J. Guiteau (President Garfield's assassin) and in 1907 at the trial of Harry K. Thaw for the shooting of the architect Stanford White. Charles W. Burr's appointment to the chair of mental diseases marked the university's recognition of psychiatry as a separate discipline. Charles Prevost Grayson was named clinical professor of laryngology and rhinology (newly recognized as a distinct specialty from otology). Among the graduates at this time was William Carlos Williams (1906). He later conducted his practice at Rutherford, New Jersey, also winning fame as a poet. In 1963, he was awarded the Pulitzer Prize for poetry.

During the early years of the present century, when the advances of medicine were great — "new discoveries in biology and biochemistry that would rapidly alter the physician's whole outlook" — the School of Medicine maintained its supremacy. William Pepper III became dean in 1912, remaining 33 years — a time separated by two world wars that once again changed the face of medicine. It was a period when advances in medical science were greater than ever before, and the school shared in these changes in teaching, research and patient care.

The faculty of the School of Medicine could well be called "doctors to the Presidents." William Shippen, Jr., was George Washington's "family doctor." D. Hayes Agnew watched over the dying James A. Garfield, and I. S. Ravdin, then John Rhea Barton Professor of Surgery, and later vice-president for medical affairs at the university, was a consultant during surgery to Dwight D. Eisenhower.

ALFRED NEWTON RICHARDS MEDICAL RESEARCH BUILDING
37th Street and Hamilton Walk

This spectacular building — one of the great contemporary structures in the world and the only one standing in his adopted city designed by the late, great architect Louis Kahn — houses the research

ALFRED NEWTON RICHARDS MEDICAL RESEARCH BUILDING

facilities for the departments of microbiology, physiology, human genetics and research surgery of the School of Medicine of the University of Pennsylvania and for the Johnson Foundation for Medical Physics. Placed strategically to benefit from the old-world intimacy of Hamilton Walk on one side, it faces the green lushness of the botanical garden on the other. The garden itself is an almost secret place, known to the students and faculty, but seldom to those outside Academe.

Alfred Newton Richards, for whom it is named, joined the faculty of the School of Medicine in 1910 as professor of pharmacology. A man deeply interested in physiology and chemistry, he was eminently suited to build a department of experimental pharmacology. He "taught pharmacology as a basic discipline, permeating and illuminating fundamental concepts of bodily function, established new standards of teaching which have guided two generations of medical teachers in Pennsylvania and throughout the country."

Internationally known for highly original and fundamental research on the kidney, he was vice-president of medical affairs at the university from 1939 to 1948. (A charmingly humorous caricature of him by Wyncie King is in the College of Physicians of Philadelphia.) During World War I he spent part of his wartime years in England with the British Army Medical Corps and in this capacity led a laboratory group investigating the nature and treatment of wound shock. During World War II he headed the Committee on Medical Research of the United States Office of Scientific

Research and Development and it was under his direction that the mass production and distribution of penicillin was carried out. (The availability of penicillin greatly affected the timing of Allied war operations.)

An expression of the genius of one man, Louis Kahn, the building is also a tribute to the contributions to medical science of another—Alfred Newton Richards.

THE WISTAR INSTITUTE OF ANATOMY AND BIOLOGY
36th and Spruce Streets

This, the oldest independent biomedical research institute in the United States, owes its existence to another generous Philadelphian with foresight and the desire to increase man's knowledge of science. In this case he was General Isaac J. Wistar, who in 1892 established the institute to house the collection of anatomical specimens and preparations amassed by his great-uncle Dr. Caspar Wistar.

This museum of anatomy and biology is open to the public (Monday-Friday, 10:00-4:00, except legal holidays; children must be accompanied by an adult) and contains the unusual and visually appealing collection of Dr. Wistar and his assistant, Dr. William Edmonds Horner. Skeletons show the development and growth of humans, as well as deviations in anatomy and the evolution of posture. Skeletons also show experiments in dog cross-breeding and growth in rats. Other exhibits illustrate the development of the embryo and the fetus.

Since its opening in 1894, when it was equipped with laboratories and facilities to enable investigators to study comparative anatomy and experimental biology, the institute has achieved world status, its influence ranging far beyond Philadelphia. Located on the campus of the University of Pennsylvania, although an entirely independent institution, its scientists have made important medical discoveries and have contributed vitally to the study of disease. In 1957, the institute was reorganized through grants from federal and state governments and private foundations. It was modernized, new staff was recruited and the emphasis was shifted from the study of anatomy to basic biomedical research with particular emphasis on biology.

The study of the transformation of normal cells into malignant cells by a cancer virus and the detection by cell fusion techniques of cancer viruses in the cells in which they have been present silently for many years are important aspects of the institute's research. A new cancer research facility was dedicated in 1975. Partially funded under the 1971 National

Cancer Plan administered by the National Institutes of Health, it was built at a cost of over $5 million and contains 51 laboratories, as well as the scientists' offices and ancillary facilities—warm and cold rooms, 150% increase in the existing animal colony and modernization of washing and autoclaving facilities. The Boyer Laboratories are in honor of the late Francis Boyer, former president of the board of managers and chairman of SmithKline Corporation.

Some of the finest examples of contemporary fine arts, crafts and decorative arts have been used in the new building. "The Wailing Woman," a sculpture created for the foyer by Vanya Radauš (1906-1975) and presented by the Institute of Immunology, Zagreb, Yugoslavia, portrays the plight of the sick and distressed of the world and was conceived as an inspiration to scientists. The Polish Room, a conference room and gift from the Societe Polonia and the Central Union Workers Productive Cooperatives of Poland, provides an entry into a Polish milieu. The hand-carved chairs and table, the woven hanging with the White Eagle of Poland worked into it, the blue and white ceramic chandelier and sconces, the handwoven draperies at the window, the mural by one of Poland's finest contemporary weavers, even the linen covering the wall itself, were all created in Poland for this room.

La Fondation Merieux, Lyons, France, contributed the Merieux Room, another conference room, in memory of Simone, wife of Dr. Charles Merieux. Here a magnificent 17th century Aubusson tapestry dominates the room. So that nothing else detracts, simple, functional furniture and an oak hexagonal parquet floor were designed to complement it.

Over 125 scientists from foreign countries have come to the institute for study periods of often more than a year. The long-range objective of the institute's program is the prevention of disease through the investigation of cellular and subcellular mechanisms operative in a broad spectrum of human diseases.

SCHOOL OF VETERINARY MEDICINE OF THE UNIVERSITY OF PENNSYLVANIA
3800 Spruce Street

Once again, Benjamin Rush was responsible. This time not for aiding yellow fever victims or signing the Declaration of Independence, but for suggesting the School of Veterinary Medicine of the University of Pennsylvania.

In 1807, when lecturing at the university's School of Medicine, he spoke "On the Duty and Adventures of Studying the Diseases of Domestic

Animals, and the Remedies Proper to Remove Them." He told his students: "[Give] the subject your attention in future studies. By acquiring this kind of knowledge you will add to the resources of medicine as far as it relates to the human body; and by disseminating it gratuitously in your neighborhood you will become the benefactors of your country."

Rush was the first to realize that it was necessary to give instruction in veterinary medicine in the same manner as it was given in human medicine. The first school of veterinary medicine was established in Lyons, France, less than 50 years before (1762); in London, only a few years prior to Rush's appeal, another had been opened.

In 1811, Judge Richard Peters, president of the Philadelphia Society for Promoting Agriculture (of which Rush was a member), authorized a committee to "prepare a plan for a course of veterinary lectures with an estimate of the expense necessary to commence the establishment." This pursuit of knowledge in the field of veterinary medicine was to continue over 75 years, from Rush's initial announcement until a school was actually opened.

Robert Jennings (who was studying under Thomas J. Corbin, "a veterinary surgeon of this city") delivered a course of lectures during the winter of 1846 to small classes of students from the city's several medical schools who hoped to practice in agricultural districts. He repeated these every year until 1850. Jennings obtained (April 15, 1852) a charter from the Pennsylvania Legislature for the Veterinary College of Philadelphia – the first charter for an institution of this character issued in the United States.

It has been disputed whether it was the first veterinary school in the country on the grounds that it was never really established and never had a suitable building or equipment. Its organization was opposed, moreover, by all veterinarians of the city, except four who joined the faculty. The college opened in November 1853, but there were no students. Jennings, not to be thwarted, tried again in 1857. Again no students appeared that year, nor the next; but two finally enrolled in 1859. The college limped on until 1866. It closed when veterinarians appealed to the Legislature for the charter for still another school – the College of Veterinary Surgeons. It was granted April 11, 1866, but this college closed after two years. The mortality rate among veterinary colleges was high in Philadelphia.

Seventy years after Rush's initial plea, another Philadelphian, Horace J. Smith, the manager of an animal farm known as George's Hill (at 52nd Street and City Line Avenue), recognized the danger of an inefficient or insufficient veterinary service. He was convinced that a course in animal disease should be given to medical students and that the most economical plan would be to organize a veterinary department in a medical college. He accordingly wrote to Dr. William Pepper, professor of clinical medicine at the University of Pennsylvania, asking if the trustees and medical faculty "would be likely to approve of having a chair of Veterinary Science established in connection with the University of Pennsylvania."

When the trustees resolved to establish one or more veterinary professorships, Smith began efforts to raise the endowment. He was backed in this by Dr. S. Weir Mitchell.

A Philadelphia publisher of distinguished medical books—Joshua B. Lippincott—made the first contribution of $10,000 in 1882. (There was only one greater and only one other as large.) These enabled the university to erect a two-story stone and brick building where Pine Street (now Hamilton Walk) and Guardian Avenue joined at 36th Street. The school opened on October 2, 1884, as the eighth department of the university (since 1909 "departments" have been known as "schools"). Twenty-nine students were enrolled, but only 10 of these graduated in the first class in 1887, with the degree of Veterinary Medical Doctor. There were two lecture rooms (one in the form of an amphitheatre), a museum, library and soon afterward a dissecting room. In 1885, another building was added for hospital purposes, as well as a small animal hospital in 1892. Dr. Rush Shippen Huidekoper, the director of the school from 1883 to 1889, saw it through its formative years and was responsible for much of its early growth. (In the first five years neither Dr. Huidekoper nor the faculty members received salaries.)

The pharmacy was in charge of Dr. Leonard Pearson, first resident veterinarian appointed in 1890 (dean, 1892-1909). In 1891, Dr. Pearson made the first subcutaneous tuberculin test on a large herd of Jersey cattle — the first practical tuberculin test on cattle in America. At this time, Dr. Pearson also introduced the subcutaneous mallein test for glanders (to control glanders in horses and mules). He was also responsible for helping control communicable diseases of animals and was instrumental in helping to form the original State Livestock and Sanitary Board.

In the last decade of the 19th century, remarkable progress was made in all lines of veterinary medicine, which was rapidly becoming a science. Previous to this time, the horse had received the greatest amount of attention. Dr. Pearson held broader views; he realized the importance of animal industry in its widest sense and that the diseases of all species of animals, including poultry, should be included in the veterinarian's education and practice. Aside from the study of diseases and their prevention and cure, he taught that veterinarians should have expert knowledge of feeding, breeding and management. His claim was that a veterinarian should be "an animal engineer."

Professor Harris Allen worked in comparative anatomy and the physiology of motion in animals and birds of special interest to veterinarians. With Eadweard Muybridge, often referred to as "the father of the motion picture," he conducted experiments on the horse. Muybridge arranged a battery of 24 cameras placed one foot apart and operated by electricity on Hamilton Walk. More than 30,000 photographs were taken. *The Horse in*

SCHOOL OF VETERINARY MEDICINE, UNIVERSITY OF PENNSYLVANIA

Motion (1882), a study of animal mechanics founded on anatomy and the revelations of the camera, was the result. It settled many oft-debated questions. The pictures showed the horse pacing, trotting, cantering and running, and proved that one of the horse's hooves was always in contact with the ground.

During the period 1901-1908, Dr. Pearson and Dr. Mazyck P. Ravenal carried on research on tuberculosis, forage poisoning, osteoporosis, and foot and mouth disease—all of which brought the school worldwide recognition. An ambulatory clinic was established in 1916. Dr. M. A. Emmerson developed a method of blocking the cornvalis, which renders painless the dehorning of cattle. He was the first to recognize trichomoniasis (chronic intestinal parasitic disease) in cattle in the United States.

One legendary member of the faculty was Franze Enge, a graduate farrier from the Lungwitz School at Dresden, where he had been a demonstrator. He remained at the school until 1928, teaching forging and horseshoeing. The students were required to spend two afternoons a week in the shop, where they learned to prepare a horse's hoof, remove the shoe, forge the shoes from the mould, and put them on the living foot. Practical work also included the forging of pathological and surgical shoes.

The New Bolton Center, the 750-acre rural campus of the school, is located near Kennett Square, Chester County, approximately 32 miles southwest of the campus. (Most of the farm acreage of the center was originally obtained by Caleb Pusey through a land grant from William

Penn.) Students are assigned to the large animal hospital and clinic at the center on a rotating plan. There they work in the clinics and laboratories, but also accompany members of the clinical staff on professional calls to area farms, thus gaining field experience in the diagnosis, control and treatment of disease. Research, both basic and applied, is an important part of the program at the center.

Among the professional services are the Georgia and Philip Hofmann Research Center for Animal Reproduction, the C. Mahlon Kline Orthopedic and Rehabilitation Center, and the Alarik Myrin Memorial Research Building, housing the Jean Austin duPont library. This last contains an outstanding collection—the Fairman Rogers Library of Horsemanship. Rogers (1833-1900) was an authority on the history of the horse and one of America's foremost coaching authorities. He and his family were immortalized by Thomas Eakins in his painting "A May Morning (The Fairman Rogers Four-in-hand)." Eakins also worked with Eadweard Muybridge when he photographed the horse in motion. Gordon Hendricks, the Eakins scholar, says: "It was the first time in the history of art that animals in rapid motion were shown as they actually move, not as they were believed to move."

The School of Veterinary Medicine, the second oldest in the nation to have been established under the aegis of a university, contains the World Health Organization's designated center for training in comparative cardiology. More than 70% of the students enrolled in the school are from Pennsylvania, and two-thirds of all veterinarians practicing in the state are graduates of the school.

LLOYD P. JONES GALLERY
(in the Gimbel Gymnasium) 37th and Walnut Streets

The special world of the athlete and the man of action is nowhere epitomized to greater effect than in the small and intimate gallery devoted exclusively to the sculpture of R. Tait McKenzie (1867-1938).

Canadian-born, Dr. McKenzie received his medical education at McGill University and served in the British Army Medical Corps in World War I. A member of the faculty of the University of Pennsylvania from 1904 until his death, he retained the title of professor of physical therapy (created in the medical faculty in 1905) while also a professor of physical education.

Dr. McKenzie was a combination of the Renaissance man and the "compleat" 18th century man: a surgeon, athlete, artist, writer, sculptor and educator.

In the gallery, the sounds of today's athletes engaged in sport serve as background to the contemplation of those of the past in bronze—runners, hurdlers, skaters, punters, pole vaulters, wrestlers, divers and boxers—stopped in action during a moment in time. There is poignancy as well as vigor here: the figures are of youth of a time past, whose records have since been shattered and titles passed on to others. The sculptures in which McKenzie immortalized these men—and he was a superb portrayer of anatomy—are an exultation of life.

Open Monday-Friday, 10:30-3:00; Saturday and Sunday, 2:00-5:00.

SCHOOL OF ALLIED MEDICAL PROFESSIONS
39th and Pine Streets

Occupying the former Convent of the Good Shepherd, this school of the University of Pennsylvania's School of Medicine is devoted to the training of professionals in physical therapy, occupational therapy and laboratory technology. The 19th century walls enclosing the convent garden cannot completely hide the summer house, where in good weather the nuns sat, prayed and read spiritual works. The School of Allied Medical Professions, which became a part of the university in 1950, was then the oldest school of its kind in the world. It absorbed the Philadelphia School of Occupational Therapy, which had been founded in 1918 to meet needs resulting from World War I.

PHILADELPHIA COLLEGE OF PHARMACY AND SCIENCE
43rd Street and Kingsessing Mall

In a city noted for "the first and the oldest," the Philadelphia College of Pharmacy and Science also has the distinction of being the first and the oldest institution of its type in the Western Hemisphere. By the second decade of the 19th century, we are told, "drugs...were crude at best, and deadly at worst....Substitution, adulteration, and misbranding were commonplace. Lack of concern for sanitation in preparing, packaging and collecting drugs served often to aggravate rather than alleviate disease. Either by accident or design, tradesmen took over the dispensing of drugs. Standards for drugs were nonexistent, and no agencies, public or private, functioned to provide them."

This, then, was the state of affairs in 1821 when a group of dedicated

Philadelphia apothecaries realized "they would have to: provide instruction for the practice of the profession; develop methods for identifying and testing drugs so that adulterated and spurious specimens could be detected and rejected; and form an organization for the advancement of the profession."

The challenge was there and was met. The founders were aided, inadvertently, by the medical faculty of the University of Pennsylvania. Courses in pharmacy were to be offered at the School of Medicine and the faculty, anticipating this, proposed to grant the honorary degree of Master of Pharmacy to apothecaries domiciled or practicing in the "City and Liberties of Philadelphia" who met standards set by the faculty.

In Philadelphia, nothing accomplished more than a dedicated and vocal opposition. A group of druggists and apothecaries met in historic Carpenters' Hall on February 23, 1821. As a result, the Philadelphia College of Apothecaries was organized in March of that year. The 68 men in Carpenters' Hall envisioned an academic institution working together "to advance the character and forward the interest of the profession." This little band of men with a single idea and a common purpose laid the foundation — one day following the 89th anniversary of George Washington's birth — of the academic institution which today is known as the Philadelphia College of Pharmacy and Science and whose alumni have gone to all corners of the world to practice and teach.

The early credo could not be faulted: "To provide the means of instruction by the establishment of a school of pharmacy in which shall be taught those branches of knowledge essential to the education of an apothecary; to invite a spirit of pharmaceutical investigation and research...; to guard the drug market (and the public) from the introduction of spurious, adulterated, deteriorated, or otherwise mischievous articles...." An admirable philosophy, presaging the growth and the achievement to come.

A board of trustees was soon organized, and on April 23, just two months after the meeting in Carpenters' Hall, Samuel Jackson, M. D., was elected professor of materia medica and pharmacy, and Gerard Troost, M.D., professor of chemistry. Now that the faculty — albeit a small one — had been chosen, a physical location was needed. In July the college (like so many of its sister institutions in Philadelphia when they were starting) rented rooms in the German Society Hall at 20 South Seventh Street, just opposite the spot where the Franklin Institute would open three years later. (It was approximately where the Balch Institute stands today and just opposite the Atwater Kent Museum.) The initial lectures were held on Friday and Saturday evenings, November 9 and 10, 1821.

By March 1822, the Pennsylvania Legislature passed an Act of Incorporation, and the name of the college was changed to the Philadelphia College of Pharmacy. Among the early faculty members was George Bacon Wood, a young Quaker physician, who was named professor of chemistry in 1822 to succeed Gerard Troost, who had one strike against him that

108

obviated his being a successful teacher: his thick Dutch accent. Dr. Wood is remembered for his contribution to the development of *The United States Pharmacopoeia*. Soon afterward, in 1825, the first issue of the *Journal of the Philadelphia College of Pharmacy*, later known as the *American Journal of Pharmacy*, was issued. It is still published by the college and is now the oldest continuously published journal of its kind in America. And in 1826, the first class—all three members—graduated.

Franklin Bache, M. D., succeeded Dr. Wood as professor of pharmaceutical and general chemistry in 1831, a position he held for 10 years, until he joined the faculty at Jefferson Medical College. He worked closely with Dr. Wood on the revisions of the *Pharmacopoeia* of 1830.

The man known as "the father of American Pharmacy," William Procter, Jr., a graduate of the class of 1837, was one of those educator-scientists whose broad interests transcended his major field of endeavor. He was secretary to the Committee of Revision of the *Pharmacopoeia* in 1841, and was elected professor of pharmacy at the college in 1846. Also the editor of the *American Journal of Pharmacy*, he was one of the men instrumental in founding the American Pharmaceutical Association in 1852.

The college, starting modestly in rooms in the German Society Hall, grew slowly but with strength. By 1852, it was able to move to Filbert Street (then Zane Street) between Seventh and Eighth (it was in this building that the American Pharmaceutical Association was founded). Just after the Civil War, in 1868, the college purchased property at 145 North 10th Street.

PHILADELPHIA COLLEGE OF PHARMACY AND SCIENCE

109

This became the nucleus of a complex at 10th and Cherry Streets that was expanded in 1881, 1893 and 1907. It was to be its home until 1928, when the Philadelphia College of Pharmacy and Science (the name was changed again in 1921) moved westward and crossed the Schuylkill River as the University of Pennsylvania had in 1872. In 1870, the first laboratory for practical work in chemistry and pharmacy was established by the alumni association.

In the post-World War I period of the twenties, the Commonwealth of Pennsylvania granted the college the authority to confer baccalaureate degrees in the four professional and scientific areas of its competence — pharmacy, biology, chemistry and microbiology. Earlier, in 1915, a two-year Graduate in Pharmacy (Ph.G.) course had been instituted, but the length of this course was increased to three years by 1925 and was discontinued in favor of the four-year baccalaureate by 1932. The one-year post-Ph.G. course leading to the degree of Pharmaceutical Chemist (Ph.C.) and the Proficiency in Chemistry certificate course were discontinued in the 1930's.

Graduate degree programs were added as the college achieved increasing stature in scientific education: in 1927, the Master of Science degree was approved in all four of the college's majors; in 1933, the Doctor of Science degree in the same disciplines; in 1958, the Doctor of Philosophy degree.

The college added a baccalaureate program in medical technology in 1965. The length of the pharmacy baccalaureate program was extended to five years in 1960 and, in 1967, an additional professional program in pharmacy leading to the degree of Doctor of Pharmacy was inaugurated. Today, the college programs are accredited by the Commission on Institutions of Higher Education of the Middle States Association of Colleges and Secondary Schools, by the American Council on Pharmaceutical Education and by the American Chemical Society.

The campus, located in the University City section of West Philadelphia not far from the University of Pennsylvania and within sight of historic Woodlands Cemetery, is centered within the area bounded by Woodland and Kingsessing Avenues, 42nd and 43rd Streets. In 1967, the City of Philadelphia gave the college the property rights to Kingsessing Avenue between these two streets, and the street was closed, the roadbed removed and a mall developed leading to Clark Park.

The college's 10 handsome buildings include Griffith Hall, the C. Mahlon Kline Pharmacology Laboratories, the Joseph W. England Library, the McNeil Research Building, Rosenberger Hall, Whitecar Hall, Kline Hall, Alumni Hall-Rosenberger Auditorium and Osol Hall (the student residence hall). The studarium is essentially a museum. Here are wooden microscopes and other early ones, the fetuses of animals, a mineral collection, early medicine bottles, medicine boxes, labels, apothecary weights, flasks and beakers. There are also apprentice indentures ("Jacob

Carver, in the service of Christopher Fingel, 1747"), mortars, pestles (French, Persian and American Civil War ones), an old muller, fascinating apothecary jars, a Chinese prescription balance and early Chinese medicines, scales — both the hanging and standing variety — and a fragment of a Spanish balance found in the remains of the *Infanta Maria Teresa* in 1898.

An even larger collection of apothecary jars (the Lily-Costelo Collection) — ancient, colorful, rare, an alchemist's hoard — greets the visitor in the entrance to Griffith Hall. There is a model pharmacy, reconstructed through the generosity of J. Mahlon Buck, as a teaching laboratory for fifth-year students. And there are gardens — the Kilmer Botanical Garden and the "Garden of Remembrance" in memory of Dr. Ivor Griffith, president of the college from 1941 to 1961.

As part of the Bicentennial effort, the college is converting its museum into a historical pharmacy to house the numerous pharmaceutical wares collected by the college since 1821. The focus of the historical pharmacy will be on the important contributions of pharmacists and the profession to America's historical development from Colonial times.

Women have been students at the college for a century now. Elizabeth Marshall, the first to attend classes, did so in 1876, and Susan Hayhurst received her degree from the college in 1883. In 1968, Miss Elizabeth R. England was elected to the board of trustees, the first woman to hold membership on the board. Today, women comprise approximately one-third of the student body.

THE AMERICAN COLLEGE OF PHYSICIANS
4200 Pine Street

"Internal medicine, in 1915," according to George Morris Piersol, M.D., "occupied an uncertain status in the United States. It was the not well accepted specialty that it is today, and those who elected to enter the field were, for the most part, self-trained."

The gravity of the situation was especially apparent to Heinrich Stern, M.D. (1865-1918), who "was well aware of the chaotic and unsatisfactory state of medical education and practice in this country at the time he was a medical student, and thereafter for at least two decades."

Dr. Stern's immediate concern was that internal medicine be properly recognized and that educational opportunities in that branch of medicine be improved. A meeting in his New York offices in 1915 brought together a group of physicians who felt as he did. Earlier, in 1913, Dr. Stern attended a meeting of the Royal College of Physicians in London. That conference

111

inspired him to gather these men of medicine together, for "such an organized group of leading internists could provide much needed and significant help in raising the standards and ideals of American medicine."

Dr. Piersol noted that "Dr. Stern envisioned the establishment of an organization that would become widely available to competent physicians with a special interest in internal medicine, comparable in many respects to the American College of Surgeons which had been established in 1913."

New York was the headquarters for the fledgling organization during Dr. Stern's lifetime, but it was soon apparent that by remaining there it would have an East Coast parochial cast. In 1918, it was moved to Chicago in order to attract members from other parts of the country, but came to Philadelphia in 1926. In 1920, three women—Drs. Leila Andrews, Ada E. Schweitzer and Anna Weld—were the first of their sex to be admitted as Fellows. In Detroit, a plan was adopted in 1926 whereby the American Congress of Internal Medicine merged with the college, and members of the congress who were not Fellows of the college were accorded the status of associates of the college. (There are three classes of permanent membership: Member, Fellow and Master.)

In 1926, the decision to move to Philadelphia was made, and, after occupying several temporary headquarters, in 1936 the Georgian mansion (built 1905-1906) of the cigar manufacturer Charles J. Eisenlohr was purchased and has been the college's home ever since. (Additional wings were added in 1962 and 1971.)

The college helped establish the American Board of Internal Medicine, which accredits specialists in the field, and now includes subspecialty boards in allergy, cardiovascular disease, gastroenterology and pulmonary disease. The board also reports to the college on its activities. The college has representatives on the American Medical Association's Residency Review Committee on Internal Medicine, the Joint Commission on Accreditation of Hospitals, the Commission on Professional and Hospital Activities, the Council of Medical Specialty Societies and participates actively in many other organizations. It provides communication links between basic medical scientists, clinical researchers and those whose duty it is to apply their findings in day-to-day practice, through scientific meetings, postgraduate courses and the monthly publication of the *Annals of Internal Medicine* (circulation 72,500). It also publishes the *Bulletin of the American College of Physicians.*

No building could be more appropriate for the college's home than the Eisenlohr mansion. It has elegance, dignity and restraint and is an architectural showplace of Philadelphia. It has a splendid entrance hall and gently winding staircase, rooms that are handsome, stately yet inviting. The former living room, now the executive vice president's office, is dominated by a dual portrait by Ferruccio Panepinto of Dr. Alfred Stengel, president 1925-1927 and Dr. Charles Ferdinand Martin, president 1928-1929.

THE AMERICAN COLLEGE OF PHYSICIANS

This portrait is unusual among the many medical portraits in the city. The Wedgwood Room—reminiscent of the days of the Eisenlohrs—has blue Wedgwood medallions inset in the panels and sconces. The Edward R. Loveland Room has certainly one of the largest and most spectacular board tables in the city. The room is in memory of the man who was executive secretary from 1926 to 1960 and the only lay person ever made a Fellow of the college.

Every Philadelphia institution has its treasures. The quintessence of these at the college is the ceremonial mace, made from a branch of the plane (European sycamore) tree under which Hippocrates—the Father of Medicine—taught 24 centuries ago on the Aegean island of Kos. It was here on this tiny isle in the Dodecanese archipelago off the coast of Asia Minor that Hippocrates is believed to have been born about 460 B.C. Legend has it that he taught and practiced medicine there and developed the code of ethics to which men of medicine have pledged themselves from his age to the present. The mace has a handsome silver head and base, created by Garrard and Co., Ltd., of London, which features the Lamp of Learning, the Book of Knowledge and the gentian flower—all emblematic of medicine. On its head are the words of the Greek physician and teacher: "Life is short and the art long."

The college primarily represents the specialty of internal medicine, but it includes among its 32,000 members practitioners of nonsurgical specialties and disciplines ranging from dermatology to toxicology. For many of these, all roads will lead to Philadelphia in 1976 when the annual session of the college is held here in the Bicentennial year.

THE INSTITUTE OF THE PENNSYLVANIA HOSPITAL

111 North 49th Street

Not only was the first hospital in the United States founded in Philadelphia, but it—the Pennsylvania Hospital—was in the vanguard in the treatment of the mentally and emotionally ill. We have seen that the East Wing of Pennsylvania Hospital had accommodations for the insane soon after it was built (1755), as did the West Wing in 1796.

Dr. Benjamin Rush, who was a pioneer in the humane treatment of the insane, probably had more influence on medical thought and practice relating to the insane than any other American of his time.

"In his psychiatric work Rush broke with traditional beliefs," according to Norman Dain in *Concepts of Insanity in the United States, 1789-1865.* "He demanded that mental illness be freed from moral stigma, that the insane be treated with kindness, that their care be under the supervision of physicians, and that religious melancholia could best be cured by medicine rather than by preaching and moralizing." Rush believed psychological methods were important in the treatment of all diseases— physical as well as mental—and he emphasized psychological therapy more than his colleagues did.

There is a very human footnote in Rush's interest in the insane, although the events occurred long after his first involvement in the issue, and after his appeal for reform during the years 1789 to 1796. His son, John, suffered an emotional disturbance in 1802 and a breakdown in 1808 (having killed a close friend in a duel). He was hospitalized in Pennsylvania Hospital for the rest of his life.

Soon patients became so numerous that in 1825 a two-story brick building—known as "The Retreat"—was erected for female patients in the northwest corner (Ninth and Spruce Streets) of the hospital grounds. The situation continued much the same until 1835. The managers realized that accommodations were inadequate and saw the difficulty of caring for patients in a hospital not conceived solely for that purpose.

The managers reported to the contributors in 1836 that they had purchased a farm of 101 acres "on the Western side of the Schuylkill in Blockley Township lying between the Westchester and Haverford Roads, and within two miles of the permanent Bridge."

On New Year's Day, 1841, the new building erected on the property was finished and open for the reception of patients from Pennsylvania Hospital. Thomas Story Kirkbride, M.D., was engaged to head the Department for the Insane, later called the Pennsylvania Hospital for the Insane. No one was a more worthy successor to the mantle of Dr. Rush. Dr. Kirkbride was 31 years old when in 1840 he was asked to assume the post of physician-in-chief and superintendent. His success was so great and his identification with the department so close that the property at 44th and Market Streets became generally known as "Kirkbride's." Dr. Kirkbride and 12 other superintendents meeting in Philadelphia were responsible for the founding of the American Psychiatric Association.

Dr. Kirkbride's treatment of the patients was humane, his attitude compassionate. He was a born administrator, and he chose the attendants and nurses with care, training them and stressing that they were not keepers but aides. The surroundings were bright and cheerful, the patients given work to do — it was called "occupational therapy" a century later — and thus the Pennsylvania Hospital for the Insane grew in stature.

Kirkbride's papers reveal a physician-humanitarian well in advance of his time. They contain letters from as far away as Iowa showing interest in sending patients to the hospital because the writers knew of others who had been helped there. He insisted that his charity patients be treated as others who were paying low rates. (From 1751 to 1850, approximately 17% of the patients treated at Pennsylvania Hospital were subsidized or received care free of charge.) Because of increased patient-load, additions were made to the building, and in 1859 a new building for male patients was opened on Mill Creek at the present site.

Dr. Kirkbride was succeeded by Dr. John B. Chapin, who arrived in 1884. By 1895, women attendants were used in the men's department for the first time. On Dr. Chapin's retirement in 1911, in his final report, he urged early hospital care, pointing out that the "largest percentage of recoveries came from those whose social position and moderate circumstances did not permit the patient to be cared for in the home." He advocated more prevention, more research — two areas that are strongly emphasized today. Dr. Owen Copp, his successor, was a strong advocate of the importance of the outpatient clinic on Eighth Street. In 1914, a nurses' school for the women's department was organized and a training school for male nurses as well.

In the 1950's because the buildings were outmoded and the cost of modernization excessive, they were razed and all services moved to the present location between 48th and 49th Streets. The Institute of the Pennsylvania Hospital — the name that the Department of the Insane, the Pennsylvania Hospital for the Insane, and Kirkbride's bears today — evolved as "the natural out-growth of long thinking by the psychiatrists of the hospital." Although initially, from 1841 on, the emphasis was on mental disorder or insanity, the institute gradually concerned itself with neurosis—the adjustments of people to their families, their work and the world around them. It was for the less sick, and was then a hospital of 60 beds.

Under the direction of Dr. Earl B. Bond, who followed Dr. Copp, there was "an active program of probing into the causes of mental illness and integrating the rapidly developing specialty of psychiatry into the life of the community."

In 1931, Dr. Herman Nunberg of Vienna joined the institute for a year and instructed the staff in psychoanalysis. He was the first fully trained European psychiatrist on the staff of an American hospital. Insulin therapy was instituted in the late 1940's and it is believed that the first electroshock treatment was given at the institute—further evidence of its early progressive search for new methods of treatment.

In 1941, the Hall-Mercer Hospital (now located at Eighth and Locust Streets) was organized. Clinical facilities and staff services of the institute administer care and treatment for certain patients selected by Hall-Mercer for special treatment and research.

During World War II, these departments of the institute set up several schools to provide psychiatric courses for Navy corpsmen and nurses. It was during this period that Dr. Bond, who had become medical director of research, resumed his duties (his successor, Dr. Lauren H. Smith, was in the Army) and could report: "There is no active front in the world

THE INSTITUTE OF THE PENNSYLVANIA HOSPITAL

where a psychiatrist or psychiatric nurse of recent training at the West Philadelphia Department is not stationed. These posts extend from duty in the Surgeons General offices in both Army and Navy to Great Britain and as far as bamboo huts on the Burma-India frontier, to mud of New Guinea and the sands of Africa."

Today the buildings of the institute reflect Dr. Kirkbride's desire for cheerful, comfortable, pleasant surroundings. The individual rooms occasionally house the patient's own furniture, the many lounges scattered throughout are furnished with antiques, beautiful rugs, handsome paintings. The atmosphere is inviting. There is an absence of restraint, and the long corridors, sunny rooms and spacious lawns bespeak serenity.

The oldest structure, called the Kirkbride Building, has labyrinthine passageways leading through the maze of underground cellars to Market Street and to 48th Street. The interior of the dome—one of West Philadelphia's most amazing architectural ornaments—is a tracery of beams and narrow winding stairs terminating in a tiny cupola at the top of the dome. The view provides a spectacular panorama of the city.

The institute, with 194 beds, has 180 psychiatrists on its staff, probably more than any other hospital in the country. Two of its strengths are its education program and its residency program in psychiatry (the latter is the oldest program in the Philadelphia area and one of the oldest in the United States). On its 27 acres, it provides facilities for inpatient treatment for most psychiatric illnesses, using three types of treatment: a hospital program, psychotherapy and special biologic treatment. There is an active unit for experimental psychology, jointly operated by the University of Pennsylvania and the institute, and research is being conducted into altered states of awareness.

The Mill Creek School for adolescents (12 to 19) experiencing adjustment problems is a four-year accredited high school for students who are either patients in the institute or are on therapy with a staff psychiatrist.

The institute maintains programs for adolescents. There is a young adult program for the college-age group. Also on the grounds are the Developmental Center for Autistic Children and the offices of the Philadelphia Psychoanalytic Institute.

V Farther Out

Although Philadelphia is a homogeneous city and its character can be seen in the various neighborhoods that make up the city proper, there is no one area having a concentration of medical, pharmaceutical or veterinary places of interest. It is true that there are more of these in certain sections than in others, but they are for the most part scattered widely throughout the Greater Philadelphia area. We call this section of the book Farther Out because some of the sites discussed are in Germantown, Chestnut Hill, Southwest Philadelphia, Frankford, along City Line or in East Falls. They may be "farther out," but they are all part of the vast aggregate that makes a visitor's encounter with Philadelphia an adventure.

JOHN BARTRAM'S HOUSE AND GARDEN

54th Street and Eastwick Avenue

A continuous link with the 18th century world of the apothecary seems difficult to conceive today. Yet in this enclave in the heart of an industrial area that also has public housing, John Bartram's house and garden continue to dream quietly in the 20th century as they did almost 250 years ago.

Bartram (1699-1777) was born at the close of the 17th century in nearby Darby. With little formal education, he became world-famous in his time, and to his door came the leading botanists of the Old World and those men of science in the New who were interested in his discoveries. One of the early "plant explorers," he found his calling accidentally. He was plowing as a young man when he observed a daisy, wondered about it, picked it, examined it, and then and there determined that he would learn more of the world of plants.

The land on which the house and garden stand was purchased by Bartram on September 30, 1728 for £140. It was only 11-1/2 acres then, but he added to this through the years until his holdings eventually totaled some 300 acres. Only 29 remain today. When he bought the land, in the section called Kingsessing by the Swedes, he was a widower with two small sons.

One of the advantages of the property was an old stone cottage dating back to the Swedish settlement. The following year, Bartram remarried — to Ann Mendenhall — and extended his house, perhaps anticipating the nine children she was to bear him. In the southeast wall, near the roof, can be seen the legend "John and Ann Bartram 1731" cut into the old stone. Above the names are the Greek words for "God Save." These are not the only memorials incised into the walls. Nearly 40 years later, he again extended the house to include the study, a remarkable feat for a man of 71 who was to live but seven years more. Having lived so close to nature in his garden, in his study, and in the wilderness where he went in search of plants unknown to the settlements or the Europeans, he cut into the stone his final testament:

It is God Alone Almyty Lord
The Holy One by Me Ador'd
John Bartram 1770

John Bartram, the first to grow rhubarb in America, planted his gardens all about him; what remains stretches to the Schuylkill River below. Here are the trees, many still labeled, plants and shrubs that have survived through revolution, political upheaval and social change — the area evolved from a rural to a residential to an industrial one. Yet though his original

JOHN BARTRAM'S HOUSE AND GARDEN

domain has been diminished, his spirit, his house and his garden remain.

Bartram had little formal education, but James Logan, the Penn family's representative in America who admired him, was prompted to order for Bartram a copy of *Paradisi in Sole,* the herbal by John Parkinson. Logan had scientific interests himself and was the possessor of one of the great libraries in the Colonies. He said of this gift: "I shall make it a present to a person worthier of a heavier purse than fortune has yet allowed him. John Bartram has a genius perfectly well turned for botany."

This genius enabled Bartram to correspond with Peter Collinson in London, sending Collinson plants in return for books. The plants, carefully wrapped, often in casks, were perishable. It was a discouraging business. Many survived, but others died. Among those who beat a path to Bartram's door, either in person or by correspondence, was Peter Kalm, the Swedish naturalist who first came to America in 1748 and later published *Travels into North America.* Queen Ulrica of Sweden (sister of Frederick the Great) corresponded with him, as did Carl Linnaeus, who called him "the greatest of natural botanists in the world." In 1765, King George III named him Royal Botanist (a rare honor for a Colonial with little formal education) at a salary of £50 a year.

Known as the solitary wanderer by the Indians, Bartram traveled on horseback, often on journeys of 1,000 miles, deep into the green world of the untracked forests. He returned, unharmed by the Indians, with his saddlebags filled. Then the plants that survived the trip were set out on his ample domain. Here a new, green world flowered, within reach of the largest city in the Empire with the exception of London. One of his 11 children, William (1739-1823), shared his father's love and passion for plants. They traveled together, and as John grew older, William set out alone. His *Travels Through North & South Carolina, Georgia, East and West Florida* shed new light on the unknown forests to the south, known previously only to the Indians, an occasional trapper or the Spanish, who showed no interest in the botanical treasures of this lush paradise.

In the days when Philadelphia medicine was in its infancy, many doctors were barber-apothecaries, later doctor-apothecaries. The mixing of medicines, potions, liniments, salves and herb teas, and the crushing of root and bark enriched the apothecary's world. Much of this knowledge was possible because of this gentle Quaker whom Washington, Franklin and Jefferson called friend.

Ever apprehensive about his beloved garden, he died a few days following the Battle of the Brandywine—his death brought on by the fear that the advancing British would desecrate his ground. Lord Howe, the British commander who was the protector of Philadelphia during the occupation, did not allow this, but permitted several officers of rank to be quartered there.

The house is open to visitors, who can see John's study and examine his herbals and other books. There are herbs hanging from the beams in the kitchen as befits the home of the leading American botanist of his time, and down at the foot of the garden beside the river is the rock that formed the base of his cider press. The grape arbor, seed house, barn, stables and garden indicate the quality of the rural life in Pennsylvania at the time. His house, his garden, his world were best expressed in the words of the Marquis Barbe-Marbois: "We found a house detached and solitary surrounded by fine orchards, and decorated on the garden front by a column of rustic design. We thought it worthy to be the dwelling of the American Linnaeus."

Open every day, including holidays, 8:00-4:00. Admission to the house: $.25.

PHILADELPHIA COLLEGE OF OSTEOPATHIC MEDICINE
4150 City Line Avenue

Osteopathic medicine as a discipline marked its own centennial on the eve of the nation's Bicentennial. A complete school of the healing arts, it was founded by Dr. Andrew Taylor Still, and is an original American school of medicine encompassing a philosophy, a science and an art. In a century, it has made greater strides in a shorter period of time than perhaps any other health science. The Philadelphia College of Osteopathic Medicine, just 77 years old, is the largest of the nine osteopathic medical colleges in the United States, and the ninth largest medical school in the United States, with a highly regarded program in academic medicine.

Founded in 1898 by Mason W. Pressly, D.O. — an ordained Presbyterian minister — and Oscar John Snyder, D.O., it has graduated nearly 5,000 osteopathic physicians since it was chartered in 1899. At its founding, it was the 12th osteopathic college since the founding in 1892 of the American School of Osteopathy in Kirkville, Missouri, by Dr. Still.

The first rooms (two) were located in the Stephen Girard Office Building, 21 South 12th Street. In fact, Dr. Pressly's first two patients became students. Seven persons enrolled in the first class, and two of these graduated. Enrollment was soon healthy enough for the Philadelphia College and Infirmary of Osteopathy, as it was called, to move to larger quarters in the Witherspoon Building at Juniper and Walnut Streets.

Dr. Snyder was instructor in osteopathic symptomology, therapeutics and jurisprudence; Dr. Pressly in physiology, philosophy and principles of osteopathy, hygiene and dietetics. In the class of 1901, there were 11 graduates; eight settled in Philadelphia and its suburbs, but three went farther afield: Harrisburg, Canada and Tokyo. By 1903, the college moved to 33rd and Arch Streets in West Philadelphia, and at this time two allopathic physicians — James E. Burt, M.D., and David S.B. Pennock, M.D., joined the faculty.

Dr. Pennock, a graduate of Hahnemann Medical School, was largely instrumental in building the department of surgery. At this time, there was still a great suspicion of osteopathy as a discipline, but because Dr. Pennock had an M.D. degree, he was able to purchase necessary narcotics and anesthetics without which the surgery could not have functioned. (Another supporter of osteopathy — at least vocally — was Mark Twain who, with Dr. Pressly, argued its cause in a delegation to the New York State Legislature.) There were other advocates of osteopathic medicine, however, such as Mayor W. Freeland Kendrick of Philadelphia, and Irene Bordoni, the French musical comedy star, who were patients of Dr. Edward H. Fritsche. Dr. Frederick A. Beale was to become the first doctor of osteopathy to minister to an athletic team. Eventually he became team physician to the Frankford Yellowjackets, the first Philadelphia professional football team and a forerunner of the Philadelphia Eagles. Later Dr. Charles J. Van Ronk performed the same services for well-known baseball players (Lefty Grove) and prizefighters (Tommy Loughran and Jack Dempsey).

A crisis occurred in 1905 when the faculty of eight protested that they only received stock shares in the college instead of salaries for their services. Five of these professors presented an ultimatum, asking for the resignation of Drs. Snyder and Pressly and that the stock be turned over to them. The founders did resign, but although Dr. Pressly left Philadelphia, Dr. Snyder continued to work on behalf of the college and to push legislation in support of osteopathic medicine. (His son, Dr. Joseph C. Snyder, was a graduate of the college.) Each year on Founders' Day, a delegation from the college decorates the grave of O. J. Snyder in West Laurel Hill Cemetery, to honor the man who put the cause of osteopathic medicine above personal considerations. An O. J. Snyder Memorial Medal, awarded in recognition of leadership and service to the college, was instituted in 1953.

In spite of resistance to osteopathy in some quarters, the college grew and in 1908 it moved again to a three-story structure at 1715 North Broad Street, one block south of the Temple University campus. The struggle for recognition bore fruit when in 1909 the college became the first osteopathic college to present a full, compulsory four-year course of study. (Earlier, the college offered two-year courses, while medical colleges required three.) Dr. Snyder submitted a bill to the legislature providing for an independent Board of Osteopathic Examiners—specifically designed to head off further confusion with, or interference by, the medical examiners.

A charter was obtained for an osteopathic hospital in 1911, and the first hospital was located at 410 South Ninth Street. (It later moved to 1725 Spring Garden Street.) The college then moved to 832 Pine Street, just around the corner from the hospital-infirmary and facing the gardens of Pennsylvania Hospital.

The watershed of the formative years occurred between 1916 and 1929. A campaign in 1916 raised $60,000, and the college purchased the

PHILADELPHIA COLLEGE OF OSTEOPATHIC MEDICINE

residence of former Mayor John E. Reyburn of Philadelphia at 19th and Spring Garden Streets. Nearby was Temple University's School of Dental Medicine. A three-story 50-bed hospital was erected on the adjoining property, providing an operating room, an obstetrical room, X-ray laboratories, nursery, isolation, minor surgery and delivery rooms. But even this ample facility could not keep pace with the college's growth. In 1929—a boom year, the last preceding the Depression—the new college and hospital buildings were opened at 48th and Spruce Streets. A fine example of Collegiate Gothic architecture, the structure was designated "the most beautiful building erected in the city in 1929" by the Philadelphia Art Commission. It served as the home of the college for 45 years and is now the college's west campus and houses a major health care center for residents of the West Philadelphia community.

All this devotion to the principles of osteopathic medicine bore fruit when in 1957 the college purchased the Moss estate of 16 acres on City Line and Monument Avenues for the development of an osteopathic medical center. Since that date, the physical growth of the college has increased greatly. The Frederic H. Barth Pavilion Hospital, named for the college's president from 1957 to 1974, is dedicated to patient care, teaching and research. The H. Walter Evans Hall is a seven-level classroom, library, laboratory and research building. It was named for Dr. Evans, a member of the class of 1917 and an obstetrician and gynecologist. He has been described as "the most College-oriented and lifetime-committed alumnus." (His son, Philip K. Evans, D.O., graduated from the college in 1954.) The former Frank Moss mansion remains as the administration center. Its dark paneling, spacious rooms and charm provide a touch of the past that contrasts with the contemporary look of the other buildings. There is even a David Rittenhouse tallcase clock in the entrance hall that belonged to Peter Ozeas, who died in 1824.

The college, with a co-founder who was an ordained Presbyterian minister, had among its graduates in 1975 the Reverend Jon J. O'Brien, S.J. Father O'Brien began his internship at Georgetown Hospital, Washington, D.C., upon graduation. Women have been an integral part of the college from the beginning. Dr. Gene G. Banker, one of the two graduates of the first class in 1900, lived to within several weeks of her 100th birthday in 1969. There were women in practically every graduating class since and many joined the faculty afterward.

Today the college operates five health care centers—four in urban Philadelphia and one rural center. With the opening in 1970 of a rural health, outreach and training center in Laporte, Sullivan County, Pennsylvania, the college began an expanded program of rural health care delivery. This primary health care center provides students with in-service training, experience and exposure to the practice of rural medicine. The college educates more general practitioners than any other medical school in the United States.

124

The osteopathic profession represents 15,000 D.O. physicians. They comprise 5% of all physicians in the United States, but care for 10% of the population, or over 20 million patients.

LANKENAU HOSPITAL

Lancaster Avenue west of City Line Avenue

The revolutionary year of 1848 affected most European countries politically and economically. Germany, then a loosely formed confederation of kingdoms, principalities, duchies and city-states, was no exception. The unification that began in 1866, and would give it strength, was some years off. Emigration to the United States began in earnest because of the chaotic conditions in Germany and the desire for political freedom.

In 1849, more than 60,000 German immigrants arrived in the United States. Many of them settled in Philadelphia. They arrived debilitated by the long voyage and bewildered and frightened by strange customs and a strange language. Two Philadelphia physicians of German descent, Dr. Heinrich Tiedemann and Dr. Wilhelm Keller, felt there was need for a hospital where the German-born residents of the city could be cared for by persons speaking their native tongue. They first tried to launch such an enterprise in 1850 and again in 1853, but it was not until 1860 that the Pennsylvania legislature granted a charter incorporating The German Hospital of the City of Philadelphia. An original bylaw of the hospital specified that "all members of the medical staff shall speak German with facility."

"Penn Brook," William Norris's residence at 12th and Norris Streets, was purchased in 1861 for $20,000 to provide a hospital, but the Civil War prevented its opening. With the sick and wounded from the Union forces overtaxing its hospitals—Philadelphia was a major center for the evacuees— the federal government appropriated the new hospital before it was able to open formally. It was not until July 1866 that the trustees regained possession of it. On Thanksgiving Day—November 29, 1866—the hospital was formally opened. The first resident appointed that year also served as apothecary. In its original bylaws, the hospital initiated what is believed to be America's first hospitalization insurance when it provided: "Unmarried persons paying regularly 25 cents a month shall be entitled to free admission as patients."

A trustee from 1866 was John Dietrich Lankenau (1817-1901), born in Bremen, Germany, the son of a prosperous importer. His wife was Mary Jane, daughter of Francis M. Drexel, the Austrian portrait painter who founded one of America's great banking houses. Lankenau was elected

125

president of the board of trustees in 1869, and the first era of the hospital's expansion began.

In 1872, a new property at Corinthian and Girard Avenues, opposite Girard College, was purchased; and by 1884, adjacent properties had been added and a great number of new buildings had been erected. In the spring of that year, too, seven Lutheran deaconesses, trained at Kaiserswerth, arrived from Germany to take charge of the hospital's nursing service and internal management. Replacing inadequately trained domestics — who in that era provided the nursing care in most American hospitals — the deaconesses soon earned for the German Hospital a reputation for superior patient care. In 1899, the deaconesses started a hospital school of nursing which has grown to an enrollment of 200.

In 1874, a free dispensary service was inaugurated, and in 1877 the charter was amended "to give instruction in the science of medicine."

Among the many Lankenau physicians who gave instruction in the science of medicine, the most famous was Dr. John Blair Deaver, chief of surgery from 1897 until his death in 1931. Shortly before he joined the staff, in 1886, the hospital had installed a handsome new operating amphitheatre with a marble gallery seating 80 spectators. Here Dr. Deaver operated (and lectured as he operated) every Saturday afternoon — to a standing-room-only audience of medical students and visiting physicians. Through these Saturday afternoon clinics, he reached every fledgling physician who studied in Philadelphia. His influence was nationwide.

Dr. Deaver pioneered in the diagnosis and removal of an inflamed

LANKENAU HOSPITAL

126

appendix. Colleagues estimated that 15,000 persons owed their lives to his skill after they were stricken with appendicitis. He operated with incredible speed. Dr. Victor Heiser, a well-known public health worker who interned under Dr. Deaver in 1897, once clocked him doing an appendectomy. "From the time he started to cut until he closed the incision was seven and a half minutes," he reported.

It is claimed that over a 50-year period, Dr. Deaver performed more surgery than any other American surgeon – 200,000 operations, according to one authority. Among the thousands of medical students he trained was his son, Dr. J. Montgomery Deaver, who later followed in his father's footsteps as chief of surgery at Lankenau. Between them, the Drs. Deaver have served the hospital for 89 years.

In 1889, Lankenau established the first bacteriological and chemical research laboratories in a Philadelphia hospital. (Facilities were offered to physicians from other hospitals and the city's Board of Health.) In the following year, the hospital's chief resident was sent to Germany to study Dr. Robert Koch's revolutionary new method of treating tuberculosis. He brought back a supply of Koch's lymph and introduced the treatment to Philadelphia. In 1896, the hospital established the city's first X-ray laboratory.

The anti-German feeling aroused during World War I not only caused the British royal family to change its name from Saxe-Coburg-Gotha to Windsor, but caused the German Hospital, in 1917, to change its name to the Lankenau Hospital in tribute to its benefactor on the 100th anniversary of his birth.

Lankenau has always been in the forefront of cancer research. In 1925, Dr. Stanley P. Reimann (1891-1968) established at the hospital the first research center to study cancer as a problem of abnormal growth. He persuaded Philadelphia merchant Rodman Wanamaker to donate funds for a research building and appointed Dr. Frederick S. Hammett, a physiological chemist, as scientific director. In 1930, a satellite laboratory was established at North Truro, Massachusetts. Here, Lankenau scientists investigated the mechanisms of metabolism and studied cell growth in simple forms of marine life. Later, the Lankenau Hospital Research Institute moved to new headquarters in Fox Chase, and in 1958 became a separate entity, the Institute for Cancer Research. ICR continues to be one of the country's outstanding centers for basic cancer research.

Soon after the cessation of hostilities of World War II, it was evident that the vast Lankenau complex of Victorian buildings was obsolete. Rather than modernize the old buildings, which were not fireproof, the hospital after an extensive survey of Philadelphia's medical requirements learned of the need for a general hospital in the vicinity of City Line and Lancaster Avenues. It was reported to be the second-fastest-growing area in the United States, with 250,000 people within a two-mile radius in which no hospital was located.

The Overbrook Golf Course was purchased—a 93-acre tract—and the new facility was constructed at a cost of $11,300,000, opening in 1953. It required the use of practically all unrestricted endowment funds accumulated since 1860—an unprecedented but courageous move on the hospital's part. The benefits have more than repaid the risk. The 425-bed hospital has a staff of 250 physicians and cares for approximately 15,000 inpatients annually. The Medical Science Building houses special patient units as well as a research center where pioneering studies are made in the fields of cardiovascular diseases, cancer and metabolic disorders. In 1953, the hospital installed the country's first cobalt unit for the treatment of cancer, and in the same year established the first hospital-based health museum in the United States.

Lankenau Hospital in 1966 affiliated with Thomas Jefferson University. The hospital is a major teaching affiliate of Jefferson; most of the college's students rotate through Lankenau for their clinical training.

Despite its growth from the simple Norris homestead to the facility which dominates the countryside surrounding it, Lankenau still retains the atmosphere of warmth and concern created by the early deaconesses. Inscribed on a bronze plaque in the hospital's lobby are the words by which John Lankenau lived and which have remained the hospital's own motto: "The life you live for others is a life not lived in vain."

FRIENDS HOSPITAL
Roosevelt Boulevard at Adams Avenue

The Quaker ethic, which after almost 300 years still permeates Philadelphia life, was responsible for many of the charitable and humane institutions in William Penn's "Holy Experiment." Not the least of these is Friends Hospital, the oldest private psychiatric hospital in the United States.

Thomas Scattergood, a minister of the Society of Friends, had in 1799 visited the York Retreat, an English mental institution founded by Quakers seven years before. The humane methods of treating the insane so impressed Scattergood that on his return to Philadelphia he extolled the virtues of such an institution to his fellow Quakers.

A tradition of involvement in such matters among members of the Society of Friends goes back as early as 1669, when George Fox, founder of the movement, advised Friends to provide "a house for them that be distempered." During the 18th century, a number of Quakers were involved with the founding of Pennsylvania Hospital (1751), which from its beginning provided care for the insane.

This tradition and Scattergood's tenacity caused him in 1811 to propose at the Philadelphia Yearly Meeting "to make provision for such of our members as may be deprived of the use of their reason." Two years later, 52 acres of open farmland were purchased in Frankford, then a small rural community entirely separate from Philadelphia. The main building of Friends Asylum was opened on "Fifth Month, 15th day" (May 15, 1817) when Isaac Bonsall recorded in his journal: "This day the house is considered as open [for patients]... but none came."

In this simple, direct statement of the quiet day-by-day events of his years as superintendent (1817-1823), Bonsall begins to tell that clover seed was planted, as were cherry trees, cedars, pear and plum trees, pumpkins and asparagus. He also records the arrival of Hannah Seal, the first patient, on May 20, who "appears to be of the melancholy cast." Hannah Jones, "a very noisy patient," and John Haworth, "harmless but very filthy," came soon afterward. Samuel P. Griffitts, whose name we have encountered before, was named consulting physician.

Bonsall, not professionally educated, was a compassionate and understanding man; he, his wife and children brought the patients into their own family group, eating with them and sharing the tasks about the house and property. There were small crises — runaways, broken windows and furniture, and John Haworth refusing to bathe (a shower was installed on July 12 — a startling innovation for the time) but the group soon began to knit together. From the beginning, work was prescribed — farming for the men, household chores for the women — and the beginnings of occupational therapy were laid down.

One of the early resident physicians (1832-1833) at Friends Asylum was Dr. Thomas S. Kirkbride, a graduate of the University of Pennsylvania School of Medicine and a nephew of Joseph Jenks, one of the board of managers. He was later to do his remarkable work at "Kirkbride's," the Institute of the Pennsylvania Hospital.

Before the 1830's, the asylum operated at half its capacity of 40 patients. Only Quakers were admitted until 1834, when a decision was made to make the asylum a nonsectarian one. Before 1834, there had been some experimentation; between 1835 and 1865 extensive innovation and improvement in moral management and a marked change in conventional medical practice were undertaken. Moral treatment — so characteristic of the Quaker attitude toward the mentally ill — was administered at Friends, an asylum well suited to its practice and strongly committed to its theory. While moral therapy was used, the staff also employed orthodox medical treatment extensively.

The members of the Society of Friends are a quiet people, going about their works of social reform in a similar fashion. The evolution of Friends Hospital has been a steady one, as befits a Philadelphia Quaker institution. Once the work was understood and successfully launched, it was carried on for over 150 years in a quiet manner.

There were innovations, of course, such as the circular railway in 1835, which was installed on the front lawn for the patients' pleasure; in 1859, a new apothecary shop was opened; a greenhouse in 1879; a convalescent cottage in 1885 in Atlantic City. In 1913, when the hospital was 100 years old, the anonymous historian of its first century of progress stated: "From the hospital standpoint, there are two distinct functions respecting the patient to keep in mind: (1) the treatment of the disease, and (2) the exacting responsibility of caring for a helpless and dependent person, which in the highest degree appeals to the sympathy of the management....Fear should be conquered, doubt dispelled and despair eradicated. In the soil from which they have been uprooted should be planted the seed which shall spring up into hope, courage, contentment, equanimity and self-reliance."

Today, the hospital's policy is to reduce class distinctions and create a family atmosphere. The staff searches for a motive for behavior, rather than merely tolerating, punishing or tranquilizing it. However, depression, schizophrenia and some other illnesses are now treated with a combination of medication and other forms of therapy as well as with psychotherapy.

In 1973-1974, 1,720 patients were admitted for treatment. In 1975, the hospital announced a construction program, which will phase out 96 beds located in areas of the institution that are older and replace them in one of two new buildings, thus maintaining the hospital's 178-bed capacity. There will be a new gymnasium-auditorium as well. Still primarily a residential institution, although there is a trend toward outpatient therapy, the hospital now operates at more than 90% of capacity. New programs instituted in recent years cover psychogeriatrics (for people aged 65 and over suffering from psychosis associated with cerebral conditions and depressive disorders) and a young people's unit (for those 13 to 21 afflicted with schizophrenia, transient situational disturbances or depressive disorders).

The gardens and grounds of Friends Hospital are nothing short of being an arboretum. From Isaac Bonsall's time, planting has continued. The first formal plantings of azaleas in 1929 have increased today to 38 varieties — "drifts of similar colors, with some irregularities to give the whole a more natural look," and the trees, shrubs, flowers all conspire to make the grounds most delightful and therapeutic for the patient. Boxwood, horse chestnut, crab apple, dogwood, Japanese flowering cherry and magnolia abound. In 1938, the gardens were opened to the public for the first time. Each year — usually the last weekend in April and the first two in May — when the azaleas are at the height of their blooming period, thousands of visitors roam the gardens. In 1974, over 20,000 found their way here. One of the oldest forms of activity therapy known is horticultural therapy. The hospital has long had a very active program.

Philadelphia has grown outward, surrounding the once rural village

FRIENDS HOSPITAL

of Frankford. Today a vast highway, with a never-ending line of traffic, stretches past "Old Main," the original building opened in 1817. Yet with the changes in the city and the treatment of the mentally and emotionally ill, Friends Hospital, in the words of its director, William P. Camp, M.D., has discovered "our reason for being is precisely the same as when the hospital was founded. All of us here feel very strongly that we are working with people, not 'cases.' To think in terms of 'cases' would be counter-productive. For if you assign a label to a patient, then you have stereotyped him, and you lose the close, caring touch that is so vital."

THE MEDICAL COLLEGE OF PENNSYLVANIA

3300 Henry Avenue

Those institutions born *in extremis*, rather than founded for other reasons—even to fulfill a local need—do not usually have an easy road to achievement. This can be said for The Medical College of Pennsylvania, founded in 1850 as The Female Medical College of Pennsylvania and, paradoxically, the dream of a man who was himself not a doctor. William J. Mullen was typical of many Philadelphians of his time: he was

zealous, possessed of an ideal, and in his thinking in advance of his generation. A man of vision, philanthropy and public spirit, he believed "women
needed not grudging admission to co-educational colleges but a medical
college of their own."

The Quakers were responsible for the liberal feeling that prevailed
in certain segments of Philadelphia life. The city was then the center of
medical education in the United States and the spirit of reform for women
was in the air as a result of a meeting at Seneca Falls, New York, in 1848,
which was sparked by Elizabeth Cady Stanton. Such women were in Philadelphia, too—those who sought equal rights: Lucretia Mott, the Quaker
reformer, and Sarah Josepha Hale, the influential editor of Godey's Lady's
Book. Medicine was in many instances in a mediocre condition and a number of the country's medical schools were inferior. There were women
spirited enough to press for admittance to the city's existing medical schools.
Certain male doctors—many of them Quakers—supported the women's
cause, which was in time to result in reform, education and achievement.

A first meeting was held in Merchant's Hall at 227 Arch Street.
Mr. Mullen spent $1,564.72 to purchase the unexpired lease on, and equip,
two rooms in the building. Forty women attended the opening lectures,
with eight seeking M.D. degrees. This small group, starting quietly, was to
pave the way for the founding of the medical college of today. In that era,
before the founding of the college, women who wished to study medicine
were forced to do so in doctors' offices under tutelage, rather than in a
medical school. Such preceptorships, while preferable to no medical education at all, were hardly the best way.

From the beginning, the college attracted superior women, and they
were fortunate in having a number of prominent citizens interested in the
new venture. Mrs. Hale, whose influence was considerable and widespread,
was interested in the undertaking, as was Thaddeus Stevens, the Representative from Pennsylvania who also fought for equal rights for the Negro.
But all was not smooth sailing.

When time for the first graduation arrived in 1851, just 14 months
after the opening session, the protest on the part of the men of Philadelphia
was so great that police reserves had to be called out to maintain order at the
graduation ceremonies in Musical Fund Hall. One of the graduates of this
class, Dr. Frances Mitchell, returned to England, carrying the college's
message abroad.

A beginning had been made, and although it was often an uphill
battle, more and more women entered the college. Interestingly enough, in
the 45 years between 1850 and 1895, 18 other medical schools for women
were founded in the United States. By 1910, only one—by now known as
The Woman's Medical College of Pennsylvania—had survived.

The Civil War brought about a crisis, forcing the college to close
for one year. In 1861, The Woman's Hospital was founded by Ann Preston,

M.D., class of 1851, the college's first woman dean, who guided it through the troubled war years. The following year the college and the hospital, though separate institutions, were under the same roof, and the students and interns later attended clinics at Philadelphia Hospital and Pennsylvania Hospital. In 1863, Dean Preston established the first school of nursing in the United States. Classes were held in Woman's Hospital.

By 1867, the college had changed its name to The Woman's Medical College, and in that same year Rebecca Cole became the first black woman to graduate from the college and the second in the United States, a rarity then and for many years to come.

Although women were allowed to study medicine, there was no place in America where they could study surgery, so Dr. Emeline Cleveland, class of 1855, pursued her studies in Paris. Graduating from the Maternité there with highest honors, she was the first chief resident at Woman's Hospital. She was also the first woman to perform an ovariotomy. For two years she served as dean after Dr. Preston retired.

Despite the fact that they had achieved M.D. status, women still encountered resistance, especially from men. The Philadelphia County Medical Society would not admit them to membership, although Dr. William Corson and his son, Dr. Hiram Corson, took up the colors in their behalf. The Montgomery and Lancaster County Medical Societies did admit women, dissenting with the Philadelphia organization. By 1866, the board of corporators of the college appealed to the Medical Society of the State of Pennsylvania, but it was not until 1871 that the state medical society decided to rescind the resolution of The Philadelphia County Medical Society. Finally, in 1888, Dr. Mary Willets of Swarthmore, Pennsylvania, an alumna, was admitted to membership. Eighty years later, Dr. Katharine R. Boucot Sturgis, another alumna, served as the first woman president of The Philadelphia County Medical Society. It took almost a century for the spirit of change to work this miracle.

In 1868, when Isaac Barton, a board member, left a sizeable bequest to the college, a new and larger home was built at 21st Street and North College Avenue, next to The Woman's Hospital. This structure, with its lecture rooms, museums, dissecting rooms and laboratories, gave the college permanence. It was a coming of age. This was to be its home until 1930, when an 11-1/2-acre tract was purchased in the East Falls section of Philadelphia and the college moved to its present location. (Alexander Hamilton once selected this site as a possible location for the Capitol had Philadelphia remained the nation's capital city.)

In the intervening years, a small maternity hospital was opened (1903) on Washington Avenue. The college hospital established a school of nursing in 1908. Since 1930, the college has grown in importance and its sphere of influence has touched every segment of the world medical community. There were, of course, crises. During the Depression the college could not

THE MEDICAL COLLEGE OF PENNSYLVANIA

pay the salaries of the six full-time professors required by the American Medical Association and philanthropic citizens came to the rescue. In 1946, Dean Margaret Craighill urged a merger with Thomas Jefferson University. The controversial proposal was voted down by the board of corporators, resulting in the resignation of many board members. During this period, Marion Spencer Fay, Ph.D., became dean and later president.

In 1969, a few men students were accepted at the college for the first time. In 1970, the school's name was changed again, this time to The Medical College of Pennsylvania. This indication of change is the touchstone of the college's philosophy. Its aims — quality medical education and medical care for a growing population — are evidenced in its teaching of doctors, nurses, postgraduate students in related scientific fields and medical technicians.

The college's list of accomplishments is as impressive as it is endless: pioneering work in fetal heart monitoring (1965), the first medical school training for inactive physicians (1968), the first medical school emergency heliport in Philadelphia (1970), the first approved internship for acute care medicine (1970).

Since 1850, the college has graduated 3,437 M.D.'s and 928 nurses. Many have contributed in unique ways. Dr. Clara A. Swain, class of 1869, was the first woman American medical missionary. The first women physicians to practice in Canada and the Philippines were alumnae. The first Indian Brahmin woman in the word to do so received the M.D. degree in 1886. Dr. Catharine Macfarlane, class of 1898, established the first cancer

134

prevention clinic in Philadelphia and was the first doctor in Philadelphia to use radium, which she obtained from Madame Curie, in the treatment of cervical cancer. Fae M. Adams, the first woman doctor in the regular United States Army, and Gioconda E. Saraniero, the first woman commissioned a captain in the regular United States Navy, are alumnae. And the list is ongoing.

The college has as one of its mottoes, "19th century pioneer... 20th century pacesetter in medical education for women." It continues to be the only college in the Western Hemisphere devoted primarily to the education of women in medicine. This commitment is fulfilled through such programs as its Center for Women in Medicine. With slight changes to include men, this attitude still prevails. The college founded *in extremis* has come of age — its 125th birthday has passed — and in its maturity it is still searching for new methods in medical education and better ways of caring for the sick.

SITE OF BOTANICAL GARDEN
High Street and Germantown Avenue

Germantown High School now stands on the site of an early home of Dr. Christopher Witt. The second botanical garden in America once stood on this spot, too, and two remarkable sisters with a scientific bent pursued their interests here. Elizabeth Carrington Morris was a botanist and Margaretta Hare Morris, a naturalist. Margaretta is said to have been the first woman elected to membership in the Academy of Natural Sciences. Her investigation of the habits of the 17-year locust enabled her to predict its reappearance.

WYCK
6026 Germantown Avenue

Its distinction derives from the fact that the oldest part of this rambling house was built in 1690, seven years after the founding of Germantown (which was incorporated into Philadelphia in 1854). This makes it the oldest house in Germantown. It was the home of nine generations of the Jansen, Wistar and Haines families (the house passed down at times through the female line, hence the change in family names) until 1973, when it was turned over to a historical trust. Opposite is The Laurens, the summer home of Dr. William Shippen, Jr.

WYCK

In October 1777, when the Battle of Germantown raged up and down Germantown Road (later Main Street, then Germantown Avenue), Wyck became a British emergency hospital and surgical theatre. The lawns and gardens we see today were strewn with the bodies of the wounded. The sound of cannon, horses' hooves, muffled shouts and sporadic rifle shots were the background accompaniment as doctors bandaged the wounded and ministered to the dying.

For visiting hours, call (215) 848-1690. Adults, $1.00; children, $.50.

MORRIS ARBORETUM
Hillcrest Avenue between Germantown and Stenton Avenues

The American answer to the splendor of Kew is found in the Morris Arboretum in Chestnut Hill, for this enchanted garden bordering the Wissahickon Creek is a counterpart of its British cousin along the Thames.

Originally the estate of John Thompson Morris and his sister Lydia, the ground was purchased in 1887 and named "Compton." (They also owned an adjacent property, "Bloomfield Farm," across Northwestern Avenue in Montgomery County, and this is part of the arboretum as well.) The Morrises were impassioned collectors of trees, plants and shrubs and soon the rolling acres were transformed into a superb woodland.

John Morris, who was more interested in horticulture than botany, died in 1915, Lydia in 1932. Her will provided for the establishment of the arboretum and funds for its maintenance. (She also left the City the charming 18th century farmhouse, "Cedar Grove," which is now in Fairmount Park.) The arboretum was opened the following year and is owned by the Morris Foundation, but is administered by the University of Pennsylvania. Since its opening, it has been a prize legacy that Philadelphia shares with visitors from all over the world.

Of special interest to physicians and pharmacists is the Medicinal Garden, established in 1957 by a grant from the Founders Fund of the Garden Club of America. Here, in neatly patterned beds, grow the most common plants that are used medicinally today. (Early physicians and doctor-apothecaries had a firm knowledge of botany.) Among them are *Camellia sinensis* (tea plant), *Cinchona ledgeriana* (ledgerbark cinchona), *Colchicum autumnale* (autumn crocus), *Coffea arabica* (Arabian coffee), *Digitalis purpurea* (foxglove), *Rauwolfia serpentina* (Java devilpepper), *Ricinus communis* (castor bean) and *Strychnos nux vomica* (nux vomica, poison nut).

Sweeping vistas lead the eye to the many plant treasures within the 175 acres. The Morrises admired Japanese gardens, and there are several. One is a subtle "Hill and Cloud" garden, with gentle hummocks forming the hills, the Japanese maple providing the cloud. The Chinese elm nearby may be the largest in the United States, and was grown from a seed brought from China in early 1900 by E. H. Wilson, the plant hunter often referred to as "Chinese" Wilson. Not far from this spot is the Swan Pond, with its tiny Grecian temple at the water's edge. Monet-like reflections on the surface of the pond reach down to its depths.

Among the arboretum's glories—and they are many—is a most unusual Bark Park, with trees of differing barks; a demonstration garden; one devoted solely to the cactus family; a propagating house, in which plants are potted once they are rooted; experimental beds; a rose garden; a heather and heath garden; an oak alley (each tree has a different variety of English ivy clinging to it); a wisteria walk; a collection of conifers, which are natural dwarfs 10 to 15 years or older; and a magnificent katsura tree, the finest of its kind in the country, with its spectacular crotch trunk.

There are secluded spots, such as the bench dedicated to Samuel Baxter (arborist of Fairmount Park), as well as grand prospects. There are also hidden crannies such as the Tropical Fernery, a glass-roofed Victorian structure that is exactly as it was when the Morrises lived here. Inside is a cool, emerald world. A waterfall, a grotto (containing filmy ferns one-cell layer thick—the largest collection of them out of their natural habitat), a rustic bridge, narrow paths shrouded with ferns, and even a Buddha hidden among the green make this a shrine to the fern.

As devoted to education and research as it is to providing visual pleasure, the arboretum has both adult and children's classes. Eighty different courses are in the curriculum and recently more than 2,000 adults took advantage of them. The children take field trips and study in the arboretum. And each child can have his own individual garden plot. Under a grant from the National Park Service, the arboretum is making a study of new kinds of trees and shrubs for city parks.

Perhaps nothing typifies the Philadelphia tradition of deeding munificently to future generations than the Morris Arboretum, which is open to the public every day but Christmas, 9:00 5:00. Admission is free.

MORRIS ARBORETUM

138

INDEX

A Academy of Natural Sciences of Philadelphia,
The iii, *77-79*, 135
Adams, Dr. Fae M. 135
Adamson, Sarah 84
"Agnew Clinic, The" *53*, 55,.98
Agnew, Dr. D. Hayes vi, 11, 26, 49, 53, 98-99
Albert Einstein Medical Center—Daroff
Division (Southern) iii, *69-72*
Albert Einstein Medical Center—Northern
Division iii, 55-56, *57-60*, 70, 72
Allen, Bishop Richard 22
Allen, Dr. Frederick H. 87-88
Allen, Dr. Sara 55
Allen, Harris 104
Allentown Academy 44
Allied Medical Professions, School of
(University of Pennsylvania) *107*
All-Philadelphia Child Guidance Clinic. See
Philadelphia Child Guidance Clinic.
Almshouse (City) v, 14, 57, 67, 83
American Association of Podiatry 39
American Board of Internal Medicine 112
American Chemical Society 110
American College of Physicians, The iii,
111-114
American Council on Pharmaceutical
Education 110
American Institute of Homeopathy 44
American Medical Association 11, 24, 44, 78,
112, 134
American Pediatric Society 89
American Pharmaceutical Association 109
American Philosophical Society *10-11*, 18, 80
American Philosophical Society Library iii,
11-13, 80
American Psychiatric Association 115
American Research Hospital for Children
(Krakow, Poland) 91
American School of Osteopathy 122
Amoss, Dr. Harold Lindsay 12
Anders, Dr. James M. 51
Andrews, Dr. Leila 112
apothecaries 11, 16, 17, 30, 77, 80, 84,
107-111, 119, 121, 137
apothecary jars 111
apothecary scales 41, 111
apothecary shops 40, 41, 77, 130
Ashurst, Dr. John 40
Association of Schools and Colleges of
Optometry 62
Atlee, Dr. Washington L. 32
B Babcock, Dr. W. Wayne 55
"Babcock Surgical Clinic, The" 55
Bache, Dr. Franklin 33, 109
Bache, Dr. Thomas Hewson 11, 89

Bachmann, Anna Boll 67
Bailey, Dr. Charles P. 46
Baker, Rear Admiral Robert L. 73
Banker, Dr. Gene G. 124
Banting, Frederick G. 71
Barnes, Dr. John 77
Bartlett, Dr. Josiah 16
Barton, Dr. Benjamin Smith 11, 97
Barton, Dr. John Rhea 81, 99
Barton, Isaac 133
Barton, William Paul Crillon 17, 42
Bartram, Ann Mendenhall 119
Bartram, John 11, *119-121*
Bartram's House and Garden, John *119-121*
Bartram, William 11, 77, 121
Bates, Dr. James E. 38
Baxter, Samuel 137
Beale, Dr. Frederick A. 122
Behrend, Dr. Moses 59
Bell, Whitfield J., Jr. 96
Bergmann, Dr. Max 12
Best, Charles H. 71
Beth Israel Hospital 70
Bettering House. See Almshouse.
Bigelow, Jacob 17
Binney, Dr. Barnabus 10
Blakiston Company 24
Blakiston, Presley 24
Blockley. See Philadelphia General Hospital.
Blockley, village of 84
Boll, Barbara 67
Bonaparte, Joseph 19, 61
Bond, Dr. Earl B. 116
Bond, Dr. Thomas 11, 28, 31, 37, 83
Bonsall, Isaac 129
Boyer, Francis 102
Brown, Mary D. 58
Bucher, Mother Mary Agnes 67, 69
Buck, J. Mahlon 111
Bunker, Chang and Eng 82
Burn Center, Crozer-Chester 69
Burn Center, Saint Agnes Hospital 66, 69
Burnett, Dr. W. Emory 56
Burn Foundation of the Greater Delaware
Valley 69
Burr, Dr. Charles W. 99
Burt, Dr. James E. 122
C Cadwalader, Dr. Thomas 11, 40
Caldwell, Dr. Charles 81
Camp, Dr. William P. 131
Cardinal Krol Community Health Center 69
Carey, Mathew *24-25*, 42
Carpenter, Dr. Howard Childs 90
Carpenters' Hall *13-14*, 108

Carson, Dr. John 10
Carson, Dr. Joseph 17
Chamberlain, Dr. W. Edward 56
Chandler, Dr. William 16
Chapin, Dr. John B. 115
Chapman, Dr. Nathaniel 11, 24, 40, 78, 81, 97
Cheselden, William 42
Chevalier Jackson Clinic 56
Children's Hospital of Philadelphia, The iii, 88-92
Childs, George W. 41, 85
cholera 67
Chovet, Dr. Abraham 81
Christ Church Burial Ground 36-38
Civil War hospitals 49, 65
Cleveland, Dr. Emeline 133
Cleveland, Grover 27, 34-35
Cohen, M. (pioneer chiropodist) 38
Cole, Dr. Rebecca 133
Cole, Dr. Rufus Ivory 12
College of Philadelphia 8, 17, 38, 96-97
College of Physicians of Philadelphia, The iii, v, 11, 19, 50, 53, 79-82, 100
College of Veterinary Surgeons 103
Collins, Dr. Richard 41
Collinson, Peter 120
Conwell, Rev. Russell H. 54
Copp, Dr. Owen 115
Corbin, Dr. Thomas J. 103
Corner, Dr. George W. 96
Corson, Dr. Hiram 133
Corson, Dr. William 133
Coxe, Dr. John Redman 13
Craighill, Margaret 134
Craven, Elizabeth Irene (Mrs. Frank Allston Davis) 76-77
Craven, Robert H. 77
Crozer-Chester Medical Center 69
Curie, Marie 135
Curtin, Dr. Roland 86
Cushing, Dr. Harvey 11
Cuvier, Georges 81

D Da Costa, Dr. J. Chalmers 26-27, 84, 86
Da Costa, Dr. J. Mendez 11, 53
Darrach, Dr. James 31
Davidson, Julius 38
Davis Company, F. A. iii, 76-77
Davis, Frank Allston 76
Dawley, Almena 87
Deaver, Dr. J. Montgomery 127
Deaver, Dr. John Blair 71, 126-127
Declaration of Independence 9, 14, 36, 37, 102
dental medicine, schools of 54, 56, 98, 124
Developmental Center for Autistic Children 117
Dewees, Dr. William P. 24
Dispensatory of the United States of America, The 12, 25, 34

Dorland, Dr. W. Newman 27
Dorland's Illustrated Medical Dictionary 27
Dorn, Anna 67
Dorsey, Dr. John Syng 21
Drexel, Francis 68, 125
Drexel, Mary Jane (Mrs. John Dietrich Lankenau) 125
Drexel, Mother Katherine 68
Duché, Thomas Spence 41
Dunglison, Dr. Robley 33, 41, 81

E Eakins House, Thomas 52-53
Eakins, Thomas 34, 52-53, 106
Eastern Pennsylvania Psychiatric Institute 56
Einselen, Anne 94
Eisenhower, Dwight D. 99
Eisenlohr, Charles J. 112-113
Ellis, Havelock 77
Emanuel, Dr. Manly 57
Emmerson, Dr. M. A. 105
Enge, Franz 105
England, Elizabeth R. 111
England, Joseph W. 110
English, Dr. O. Spurgeon 56
Episcopal Hospital 69-70
Evans, Dr. Cadwalader 83
Evans, Dr. H. Walter 124
Evans, Dr. Philip K. 124

F Faith, Goldie Basch 86
Farber, Mrs. Joseph 41
Fay, Marion Spencer 134
Federal Caustic Poison Law 35
Feldstein, Dr. Adolph 58
Fels Research Institute 56
Female Medical College of Pennsylvania, The 28, 45, 84, 131
Finck, Furman J. 55
First Bank of the United States 15
Fisher, Alice 85, 93
Fitch, Dr. Albert 60
Flexner, Dr. Simon 11, 12, 99
foot and mouth disease 105
Forbes, Dr. William Smith 53
Fothergill, Dr. John 9, 12
Foulke, Dr. John 10, 40, 82
Franklin, Benjamin 8, 10, 11, 14, 19, 24, 28, 36-37, 42, 75, 80, 83, 121
Franklin Free Dispensary 70
Franklin, Sir John 9
French, John 93
Freud, Sigmund 27, 75
Friends Hospital iii, iv, v, 68, 128-131
Friends, Society of 128-129
Fritsche, Dr. Edward H. 122

G gardens 17, 18, 32, 111, 119-121, 135, 136-138
gardens, botanical 80, 82, 100, 111, 119-121, 130, 135, 136-138
Garfield, James A. 49, 99
Garretson Hospital 55

Garrison, Colonel Fielding H. 97
Gates, Dr. Thomas Sovereign 11, 94
Gates, General Horatio 14
Gay-Lussac, Dr. Joseph 81
Georgetown Hospital (Washington, D.C.) 124
Gerhard, Dr. William Wood 31
German Hospital 70, 125
Gibbon, Dr. John H., Jr. 35
Gibbon, Mary Hopkinson 35
Gilliams, Dr. Jacob 77
Gilman, Amelia 85
Girard, Stephen 15, 30
Gittings, Dr. John 91
Gleason, Dr. E. B. 27
Glentworth, Dr. Gerardus 10
Glentworth, Dr. Plunket Fleeson 81
Godman, Dr. John D. 24
Goodell, Dr. William 98
Goodman, Dr. Henry E. 49
Grahame, Israel J. 41
Gratz, Rebecca 57
Gray's Anatomy 25
Grayson, Dr. Charles Prevost 99
Greater Delaware Valley Transplant Society 60
Greatheart Hospital 54
Greene, Ryland W. 27
Griffith, Dr. Ivor 111
Griffith, Dr. John Price Crozer 89-90, 98
Griffitts, Dr. Samuel P. 10, 129
"Gross Clinic, The" 34, 53, 55
Gross, Dr. Samuel D. vi, 11, 26, 34, 49, 53
H Hackenberg, William B. 59
Hahnemann, Dr. Samuel 44, 45
Hahnemann Medical Center iii, iv, 44-47, 69
Hahnemann Medical College and Hospital 46
Hahnemann Medical College of Philadelphia 45, 46, 122
Hale, Sarah Josepha 132
Hall, Dr. Lyman 16
Hall-Mercer Hospital 116
Hamill, Dr. Samuel McC. 90
Hamilton, James 8
Hammett, Dr. Frederick S. 127
Hand, Dr. Alfred 90
Hankins, Dorothy 87
Harris, Dr. Robert 10
Hartman, David 57
Hayhurst, Susan 111
Hays, Dr. I. Minis 11, 48
Hays, Dr. Isaac 24, 48
Hebrew Relief Society 57
Heiser, Dr. Victor 127
Hering, Dr. Constantine 44
Hespelein, Rev. John B. 67
Hewson, Dr. Addinell 49
Hewson, Dr. Thomas Tickell 11, 37, 49, 81
Hewson, Dr. William 37, 49

Hewson, Mary Stevenson 37
Hill-Physick-Keith House iv, 19-21, 37
Hippocrates 113
Historical Society of Pennsylvania iv, 40-41
Holmes, Dr. Oliver Wendell 81, 82
Holmes, Justice Oliver Wendell 49
Holme, Thomas 7, 22, 74
Homeopathic Medical College of Pennsylvania 44, 45
Homeopathic Medical Hospital of Philadelphia 46
Horner, Dr. William Edmonds 11, 48, 101
Horner, Edith 85
Hospital for Sick Children (London) 89, 91
Hospital of the University of Pennsylvania iv, 27, 68, 92-95, 98
hospitals, military 49, 65, 83, 125, 136
hospitals, United States Navy 64-66, 72-73
Hugo, Charlotte Marie 93
Huidekoper, Dr. Rush Shippen 104
Humboldt, Alexander von 81
Hunt, Dr. William 49
Hutchinson, Dr. James 10, 12
Hyman, Dr. Albert Salisbury 71
I Independence Hall 8-9, 10, 31, 35, 41, 83
insane, care of 29, 83, 114-115, 128-131
Institute of the Pennsylvania Hospital, The iii, iv, 114-117, 129
J Jackson, Dr. Chevalier 11, 27, 35, 56, 94
Jackson, Dr. Samuel 50, 77, 108
Jeanes, Dr. Jacob 44
Jefferson Hospital 21, 26, 36
Jefferson Medical College v, 23, 26, 27, 32-34, 47, 52-53, 75, 84, 97, 98, 109
Jefferson, Thomas 11, 13, 33, 36, 41, 61, 121
Jenks, Joseph 129
Jennings, Dr. Robert 103
Jewish Hospital, 55, 57-59, 70, 72
Jewish Hospital Association 57
Jewish Maternity Hospital 71
Johns Hopkins University, medical school of 98
Jones, Dr. John 10-11
Jones, Dr. Robert E. 16
Jones Gallery, Lloyd P. 106-107
K Kahn, Louis 99, 101
Kalm, Peter 120
Kane, Dr. Elisha Kent 9, 41
Kearsley, Dr. John v, 37, 75
Keen, Dr. William W. 27, 34-35
Keller, Dr. Wilhelm 125
Kendrick, Bishop Francis Patrick 67
"Kinsey Report" 77
Kirkbride, Dr. Thomas Story 115, 117, 129
Kirkville, Missouri 122
Kline, C. Mahlon 106, 110
Koch, Dr. Robert 98, 127
Kolmer, Dr. John A. 56
Koop, Dr. C. Everett 92

Krol, John Cardinal 68
Kuhn, Dr. Adam 11, 96
L Lancaster County Medical Society 133
Lankenau Hospital iv, 70, 125-128
Lankenau, John Dietrich 125
Lavender, Mrs. (early midwife) 84
Lavoisier, Antoine Laurent 97
Lea & Febiger iv, 23, 24-25
LeConte, Dr. R. G. 31
Leidy, Dr. Joseph 79, 81, 97
Leidy, Dr. Joseph II 53
Leonard, Dr. Charles Lester 53, 94
Letterman, Dr. Jonathan 34
Levis, Dr. Richard J. 49
Lewis, Dr. Fielding O. 34
Lewis, Dr. Francis West 89
Liberty Bell 19
libraries 11-13, 16, 31, 40-42, 81, 104, 106, 110
Library Company of Philadelphia iv, 11, 41-42
Library Hall 11-13, 80
Linnaeus, Carl 120, 121
Lippincott Company, J. B. iv, 23, 25-26, 32, 76
Lippincott, Joshua B. 104
Lipshutz, Dr. Benjamin 71
Lister, Joseph, 1st Baron 98
Lit, Jacob D. 70
Littell, Dr. Squier 47
Logan, Dr. George 37, 41
Logan, Dr. William 42
Logan, James 120
Logan, William 42
Longshore, Dr. Anna Mary 28
Longshore, Dr. Hannah 28
Loveland, Edward R. 113
Lucchesi, Dr. Pascal F. 60
Lum, Mary (Mrs. Stephen Girard) 15, 30, 31
Lungwitz School (Dresden, Germany) 105
M McAllister, John 49, 60-61
McAllister, John, Jr. 49, 61
McClellan, Dr. George 32, 33, 47
McClellan, General George 32
McClure, Dr. William 49
McKenzie, Dr. R. Tait 75, 106-107
Macfarlane, Dr. Catharine 134-135
Maclure, William 79
Magee Memorial Hospital 46
Mann, Dr. Camillus Macmahon 77
Marshall, Charles 40
Marshall, Chief Justice John 19
Marshall, Christopher 40
Marshall, Dr. Clara 84
Marshall, Elizabeth 111
Martin, Dr. Charles Ferdinand 112
Massachusetts General Hospital 31
Medical College of Pennsylvania, The iv, 28, 45, 84-85, 131-135
Medical College of Virginia 98
medical school, coeducational 55

medical school, evening 54-55
medical schools, women's 28, 55, 131-135
Medical Society of the State of Pennsylvania, The 50, 133
Medico-Chirurgical College 76
Meigs, Dr. Arthur Vincent 89
Meigs, Dr. John Forsyth 89
Merieux, Charles and Simone 102
Metropolitan Hospital 39
midwives, 8, 41, 84
Mifflin, Thomas 80
Mill Creek School 117
Mills, Dr. Charles Krasner 99
Mills House, Robert 35 36
Minuchin, Dr. Salvador 88
Mitchell, Dr. Frances 132
Mitchell, Dr. John Kearsley 31, 75
Mitchell, Dr. S. Weir vi, 11, 18, 49, 75-76, 104
Mitchell House, S. Weir 75-76
Monro, Alexander 42
Montgomery County Medical Society 133
Moore, Dr. John Royal 56
Morgan, Dr. John 11, 12, 30, 37, 41, 42 96-97
Morris Arboretum iv, 136-138
Morris, Elizabeth Carrington 135
Morris, John Thompson 136-137
Morris, Lydia Thompson 136-137
Morris, Margaretta Hare 135
Morris, Robert 33
Morton, Dr. Samuel George 12, 78
Morton, Dr. Thomas G. 31
Moss Rehabilitation Hospital 60
Mother Bethel African Methodist Episcopal Church 22
Mott, Lucretia 132
Mount Sinai Hospital 70-72
Mount Sinai Hospital Association 70
Mullen, William J. 131-132
Musical Fund Hall 27-28, 132
Mütter Museum 19, 82
Muybridge, Eadweard 42, 104-105, 106
N National Committee for Mental Hygiene 86
National Heart and Lung Institute 95
National Institutes of Health 95, 102
Naval Asylum 64, 72
Naval Regional Medical Center iii, iv, 72-73
Nazareth Hospital iii
Nebinger, Dr. Andrew 67
New Bolton Center 105-106
Nightingale, Florence 85
Norris, Dr. George W. 31
Norris, Dr. William F. 92, 99
Norris, Isaac 42
Norris, William 125
North Philadelphia Hospital, The 54
Nunberg, Dr. Herman 116
nursing schools 54, 59, 67, 85-86, 93, 115, 126, 133

O O'Brien, Dr. Jon J., S.J. 124
Old Pine Presbyterian Church 21
Opie, Dr. Eugene Lindsay 12
Osler, Sir William, M.D. vi, 81, 85, 98
Otto, Dr. J. C. 31
Owen, Dr. Griffith v
P Pancoast, Dr. Henry 52, 94
Parke, Dr. Thomas 11, 12, 37
Parkinson, John 120
Parmentier, Nicholas S. 77
Parrish, Dillwyn 58
Parrish, Dr. Isaac 48, 49
Parrish, Dr. Joseph 48, 58
Pasteur, Louis 98
Peale, Charles Willson 81
Peale, Rembrandt 81

Pearson, Dr. Gerald H. J. 56
Pearson, Dr. Leonard 104
Pennock, Dr. David S. B. 122
Penn, Richard 8
Pennsylvania Academy of the Fine Arts 21, 53
Pennsylvania College of Optometry iii, iv,
  39, 60-62
Pennsylvania College of Podiatric Medicine
  iv, 38-39
Pennsylvania Horticultural Society iv, 16-17
Pennsylvania Hospital iv, v, 8, 9, 13, 14, 15, 18,
  21, 28-32, 37, 41, 49, 53, 57, 68, 72, 80,
  82-83, 90, 91, 93, 114-115, 123, 128, 133
Pennsylvania School of Social Work 88
Pennsylvania State Navy 72
Pennsylvania, University of iv, 8, 9, 11, 13, 18,
  23, 27, 32, 34, 37, 38, 41, 42, 53, 77, 84, 91,
  96-97, 103-104, 106, 107-108, 110, 117, 137
Penn, Thomas 8
Penn, William v, 7, 22, 31, 43, 44, 72, 74, 84,
  105-106, 128
Penrose, Dr. R. A. F. 89
Pepper, Dr. William vi, 93, 103
Pepper, Dr. William, Jr. vi, 27, 92, 98, 99
Pepper, Dr. William III 99
Philadelphia Child Guidance Clinic iv,
  86-88, 92
Philadelphia College of Apothecaries. See
  Philadelphia College of Pharmacy and
  Science.
Philadelphia College of Medicine 45
Philadelphia College of Osteopathic Medicine
  iii, iv, 121-125
Philadelphia College of Pharmacy and
  Science iv, v, 14, 34, 50, 77, 107-111
Philadelphia County Medical Society, The
  iv, 50-52, 133
Philadelphia Dental College 56
Philadelphia Dispensary 13
Philadelphia General Hospital iv, v, 51, 57,
  82-86, 93, 133
Philadelphia Hospital. See Philadelphia
  General Hospital.

Philadelphia Medical Society and Institute
  40, 50
Philadelphia Museum of Art 52, 53
Philadelphia Navy Yard 64, 72, 73
Philadelphia Psychoanalytic Institute 117
Philadelphia Society for Promoting
  Agriculture 103
Philadelphia State Hospital 16, 86
Phillips, Dr. Algernon 62
Philosophical Hall 10-11, 80
Physick, Abigail 19
Physick, Dr. Philip Syng 9, 19-21, 37, 42, 97
Piersol, Dr. George Morris 94, 111-112
Piper, Dr. Edmund B. 94
Potsdamer, Dr. Joseph B. 70
Presbyterian Hospital 70
Pressly, Dr. Mason W. 122-123
Preston, Dr. Ann 132-133
Procter, William, Jr. 109
Public Charities Association of Pennsylvania
  87
publishers, medical 23-27, 76-77
R Rand, Dr. Benjamin Howard 53
Randolph, Dr. Jacob 21
Rank, Dr. Otto 88
Ravdin, Dr. Isidor S. 94, 99
Ravenal, Dr. Mazyck P. 105
Redman, Dr. John 30, 79
Reimann, Dr. Stanley P. 127
Rhoads, Samuel 14, 29
Richards, Dr. Alfred Newton 100-101
Richards Medical Research Building, Alfred
  Newton 99-101
Roberts, Jonathan 30
Rockefeller Institute 12, 99
Rodriguez, Altagracia and Clara 92
Roentgen, Wilhelm C. 94
Rogers, Fairman 106
Root, Dr. Mary Pauline 85
Rosenbach, A. S. W. 58
Rosenbach, Morris 58
Rosenbach, Philip 58
Rous, Dr. Francis Peyton 12
Royal College of Physicians (London) 79, 111
Royal Society of London 10
Rush, Dr. Benjamin 9, 11, 12, 14, 15-16, 21,
  22, 24, 29, 31, 37, 42, 79, 82, 83, 96-97,
  102, 103, 114
Rush, Dr. James 42
Rush House, Dr. Benjamin 15-16
Rush, John (great-grandfather of Benjamin)
  16
Rush, John (son of Benjamin) 114
Rush, Susanna 16
S Sabin, Dr. Florence Rena 12
Saint Agnes Hospital iv, 66-69
Saint Christopher's Hospital 56
Saint Francis, Sisters of 66-69
Saint Joseph's Hospital 67, 70

Saint Joseph's Hospital (Lancaster, Pennsylvania) 67
Saint Mary Hospital 67, 70
Samaritan Hospital 54
Saraniero, Dr. Gioconda E. 135
Sargent, Dr. Fitzwilliam 18, 49
Sargent, John Singer 18, 49
Saunders Company, W. B. iv, 23, 26-27, 77
Saunders, Walter Burns 26, 27
Say, Thomas 77
Scattergood, Thomas 128
School of Medicine of the University of Pennsylvania v, 9, 13, 30, 32, 41, 47, 49, 53, 76, 79, 91, 93, 96-99, 100, 102, 129
Schweinitz, Dr. George E. de 27, 99
Schweitzer, Dr. Ada E. 112
Sellers, Dr. Charles 40
Seton, Saint Elizabeth Ann 67

Shephard, Dr. Mary E. 55
Shinn, John, Jr. 77
Shippen, Dr. William 17, 83
Shippen, Dr. William, Jr. 8, 11, 12, 17-18, 21, 31, 37, 83, 96-97, 99, 135
Shippen-Wistar House 17-19
Shoemaker, Dr. John V. 76
Shultz, Benjamin 17
Sims, Dr. J. Marion 34
Skin and Cancer Hospital 39, 56
Smith, Dr. Lauren H. 116-117
SmithKline Corporation 53, 102
Snyder, Dr. Joseph C. 123
Snyder, Dr. Oscar John 122-123
Solis-Cohen, Dr. Jacob Da Silva 57, 81
Solis-Cohen, Dr. Solomon 59
Speakman, John 77, 78
Spencer, Dr. Adam 8
Spiegel, Dr. Ernest A. 56
Stengel, Dr. Alfred 94, 112
Stern, Dr. Heinrich 111-112
Still, Dr. Andrew Taylor 121
Stillé, Dr. Alfred 86
Stokes, Dr. Joseph, Jr. 91
Strickler, Dr. Albert 56
Sturgis, Dr. Katharine R. Boucot iii, 52, 82, 133
Surgeons' Hall 13
Swain, Dr. Clara A. 134
Syng, Philip 9
T Temple University iii, 38, 39, 123
Temple University Health Sciences Center iii, iv, 54-57
Temple University Hospital 54, 56
Temple University Medical School 54, 56
Temple University Pharmacy School 54, 56
Temple University School of Dentistry 54, 56, 124
Thomas Jefferson University iii, iv, v, 32-35 50, 53, 134
Thomson, Dr. William 49, 53

Thornton, Dr. Matthew 16
Tiedemann, Dr. Heinrich 125
Troost, Dr. Gerard 77, 108-109
U United States Dispensatory, The 25
United States Naval Home iv, 64-66, 72, 84
United States Pharmacopoeia, The 34, 51, 80, 109
United States Sanitary Commission and Fair 40
University of Pennsylvania Medical School. See School of Medicine of the University of Pennsylvania.
V Van Ronk, Dr. Charles J. 122
van Rymsdyck, Jan 8, 31
Veterinary College of Philadelphia 103
Veterinary Medicine, School of (University of Pennsylvania) iii, 102-106
Veterinary Surgeons, College of 103
W Warner, William 84
Washington and Jefferson University 32
Washington, George 13, 34, 61, 80, 83, 97, 99, 108, 121
Washington Square 22-23, 26, 44
Way, Dr. Phoebe 28
Weiss, Dr. Edward 56
Weld, Dr. Anna 112
Wharton, Thomas, Jr. 83
White, Dr. J. William 27, 53, 94
Willets, Dr. Mary 52, 133
Williams, Dr. William Carlos 99
Williamson, Dr. Walter 44
Williamson, Isaiah 93
Wills Eye Hospital iv, 47-50
Wills, James, Jr. 47, 50
Wilson, Dr. Benjamin B. 57
Wilson, Ernest Henry ("Chinese") 137
Wistar, Dr. Caspar 11, 12, 18, 37, 41, 48, 97, 101
Wistar, General Isaac J. 101
Wistar Institute of Anatomy and Biology, The iv, 18, 101-102
Withering, Dr. William 13
Witt, Dr. Christopher 135
Wolcott, Dr. Oliver 16
Wood, Dr. George Bacon 12, 34, 98, 108-109
Wood, Dr. Horatio C. 92, 98
Woodhouse, Dr. James 97
Woman's Medical College of Pennsylvania. See Medical College of Pennsylvania.
Woman's Hospital 132
Woman's Hospital of the State of New York 34
Women's Medical Club of Philadelphia 46
Wycis, Dr. Henry T. 56
Wyck 135-136
Wynne, Dr. Thomas v
Y Yandell, Dr. W. D. 34
yellow fever 11, 12, 15, 16, 22, 23, 24, 42, 51, 80, 102
Z Zacharie, Isachar 38
Zimmerman, John 80

144